PEARSON LON

KEYSTONE

C

PEARSON English Learning System

Workbook

Anna Uhl Chamot

John De Mado

Sharroky Hollie

PEARSON

Upper Saddle River, New Jersey • Boston, Massachusetts • Chandler, Arizona • Glenview, Illinois

PEARSON LONGMAN
KEYSTONE C

PEARSON English Learning System

Workbook

Staff credits: The people who made up the *Longman Keystone* team, representing editorial, production, design, manufacturing, and marketing, are John Ade, Rhea Banker, Liz Barker, Danielle Belfiore, Virginia Bernard, Kenna Bourke, Anne Boynton-Trigg, Andrea Bryant, Johnnie Farmer, Patrice Fraccio, Geraldine Geniusas, Charles Green, Henry Hild, Lucille M. Kennedy, Ed Lamprich, Emily Lippincott, Tara Maceyak, Maria Pia Marrella, Linda Moser, Laurie Neaman, Sherri Pemberton, Liza Pleva, Edie Pullman, Tania Saiz-Sousa, Chris Siley, Lynn Sobotta, Heather St. Clair, Jennifer Stem, Jane Townsend, Marian Wassner, Lauren Weidenman, and Adina Zoltan.

Smithsonian American Art Museum contributors: Project director and writer: Elizabeth K. Eder, Ph.D.; Writer: Mary Collins; Image research assistants: Laurel Fehrenbach, Katherine G. Stilwill, and Sally Otis; Rights and reproductions: Richard H. Sorensen and Leslie G. Green; Building photograph by Tim Hursley.

Cover Image: Background, John Foxx/Getty Images; Inset, Alex Bloch/Getty Images
Text composition: TSI Graphics
Text font: 11 pt ITC Stone Sans Std
Photos: 28, James Randklev/ChromoSohm Media Inc./Photo Researchers, Inc.; 124, Hulton Archive Photos/Getty Images
Technical art: TSI Graphics

Copyright © 2013 Pearson Education, Inc., or its affiliates. All Rights Reserved. Printed in the United States of America. This publication is protected by copyright, and permission should be obtained from the publisher prior to any prohibited reproduction, storage in a retrieval system, or transmission in any form or by any means, electronic, mechanical, photocopying, recording, or likewise. For information regarding permissions, write to Rights Management & Contracts, Pearson Education, Inc., One Lake Street, Upper Saddle River, New Jersey 07458.

Pearson is a trademark, in the U.S. and/or other countries, of Pearson Education, Inc., or its affiliates.

ISBN-13: 978-1-4284-3506-3
ISBN-10: 1-4284-3506-9

Printed in the United States of America
12   17

PEARSON

Contents

Unit 1

Copyright © by Pearson Education, Inc.

Unit 2

READING 1

READING 2

READING 3

READING 4

Copyright © by Pearson Education, Inc.

Contents

Unit 3

READING 1

READING 2

READING 3

READING 4

Copyright © by Pearson Education, Inc.

Unit 4

READING 1

READING 2

READING 3

READING 4

Copyright © by Pearson Education, Inc.

Contents

Unit 5

READING 1

READING 2

READING 3

READING 4

Contents

Copyright © by Pearson Education, Inc.

Unit 6

READING 1

READING 2

READING 3

READING 4

Copyright © by Pearson Education, Inc.

UNIT 1

How can change improve people's lives?

READING 1: From *Riding Freedom*

VOCABULARY **Literary Words** *Use with textbook page 5.*

REMEMBER A **plot** is the sequence of related events in a story. Most plots contain one or more conflicts. A **conflict** is a struggle between opposing forces. It moves the story forward and makes it more interesting.

Write *yes* if each situation describes a conflict. Write *no* if it does not.

Conflict?	Situation
yes	Aliyah wants dessert but her mother tells her to study instead.
1.	The two dogs snarled at one another.
2.	Raúl picked up the tennis ball and threw it to Maria.
3.	The wind howled. I didn't want to go back into the storm.

Write one or two sentences in each row illustrating a conflict between the following person or thing.

People/Things	Sentences
two people who want the same object	*Edgar and Astrid crossed their arms. They both yelled at the same time, "That's mine!"*
4. person versus mountain	
5. doing the right thing versus doing the easy thing	

Copyright © by Pearson Education, Inc.

Read the paragraph below. Pay attention to the underlined academic words.

> During the 1960s in the United States, more and more women wanted to work outside the home. However, many faced <u>discrimination</u>. They had trouble finding work. If they did find work, they were often paid less than men. Women fought for equality by holding marches and speaking out for their rights. Over time, this helped change people's <u>attitudes</u> about women in the work force. Women finally <u>achieved</u> equality in the workplace. Today, to deny a person a job based on gender is <u>illegal</u>.

Write the academic words from the paragraph above next to their correct definitions.

Example: *discrimination*: unfair treatment of some people because of their race, ethnic group, religion, or gender

1. _____: succeeded in doing something, especially by working hard

2. _____: not allowed by law

3. _____: thoughts or feelings about something or someone

Use the academic words from the paragraph above to complete the sentences.

4. It is _____ to drive without a driver's license.

5. Different people have different _____ about politics.

6. She worked hard all her life and _____ great things.

7. Most people want to eliminate _____ in the workplace.

Complete the sentences with your own ideas.

Example: In the past, _____*my ancestors*_____ suffered from discrimination.

8. My attitude toward _____ has changed over time.

9. _____ achieved wonderful things in life.

10. I know that it is illegal to _____.

Copyright © by Pearson Education, Inc.

WORD STUDY   Double Consonants   *Use with textbook page 7.*

REMEMBER When an ending is added to a single syllable word that ends in a vowel + a consonant, the final consonant is doubled, as in *spin/spinning*. If the word has more than one syllable, the consonant is doubled if the stress is on the final syllable, as in *control/controlling*.

Add an ending as directed to each word. Write the word in the last column.

Base Word	+ Ending	= New Word
hop	-ed	*hopped*
1. sit	-ing	
2. submit	-ed	
3. pat	-ed	
4. snap	-ing	
5. shop	-ing	

Create a new word by adding the ending *-ed* or *-ing* to each word below.

Example: begin + ___*ing*___ = _____*beginning*_____

6. fasten + _____ = _____

7. spot + _____ = _____

8. omit + _____ = _____

9. slip + _____ = _____

10. clap + _____ = _____

Copyright © by Pearson Education, Inc.

> **REMEMBER** Analyzing historical context can make a text more meaningful and easier to understand. Pay attention to events, location, and characters' reactions. Think about what you already know about the events or setting.

Read the paragraph and answer the questions that follow.

The Day After

Yesterday, on September 11ᵗʰ, when the towers fell, everything was chaos. When I arrived at the soup kitchen the next morning, I was surprised by how organized the workers were.

"Are you here to help?" asked a man behind the table.

"Uh…Yeah, I am."

"Good. They need some help down at that end of the table," he said.

I started to help a woman who was putting sandwiches on plates and handing them out. Firefighters and police started to file by. Some were covered in dust. All of them looked tired. Some would eat and leave, but others would stay and talk.

At the end of the day, the man in charge of the soup kitchen came by.

He said, "Thanks for the help today. Can you come back tomorrow?"

"You bet," I said. I couldn't imagine staying in my apartment uptown. I needed to be here. I needed to help.

---

1. When does the story take place?

_____

2. Where does the story take place?

_____

3. What historical event had just happened in the place and time of the story?

_____

4. What is the main character's reaction to the events that have taken place around her?

_____

5. How can knowing the historical context of a story help you to understand its meaning?

_____

Copyright © by Pearson Education, Inc.

COMPREHENSION *Use with textbook page 14.*

Choose the best answer for each item. Circle the letter of the correct answer.

1. Charlotte pretended to be "Charley" to _____.

   a. make friends **b.** run for office **c.** run her business

2. Since she was a woman, Charlotte had to register to vote _____.

   a. disguised as a man **b.** in a dress **c.** with a male friend

3. Everyone asked Charley _____.

   a. who she would vote for **b.** why she was dressed like a man **c.** why she registered to vote

4. The men in town thought that women should _____.

   a. vote like their husbands **b.** stay out of politics **c.** fight for their rights

5. The real Charlotte Parkhurst's identity was discovered _____.

   a. by a traveler who worked with her **b.** when she tried to vote **c.** after she died

RESPONSE to LITERATURE *Use with textbook page 15.*

Write a short paragraph describing how you think Charlotte might have felt on her ride to town. Was she scared? Excited? Ready for a fight? Did she think of her friend Hayward?

_____

_____

_____

_____

_____

Copyright © by Pearson Education, Inc.

REMEMBER Sequencing words and phrases such as *first, then, next, after that, now, finally,* and *last* describe the order in which events take place. *First* introduces the first thing that happened; *finally* and *last* introduce the last thing; *then, next, after that,* and *now* introduce anything that happened in between. Most of these sequencing words and phrases take a comma after them, but *then* and *now* do not.
Be sure to use parallel structure and consistent verb tense when narrating a sequence of events.

Put the events for making a collage in the correct order. Then choose an appropriate sequencing word from the box. Be sure to use commas when necessary.

Last	Next	Then	After that	Now	~~First~~

1. _____ I cut out the pictures. _____

2. _____ I arranged the pictures on the construction paper. _____

3. _____ I got a piece of construction paper and some glue. _____

4. _____ I chose about 20 pictures from the magazines. _____

5. _____ I glued the pictures on the construction paper. _____

6. _____*First*_____, I collected some magazines. ___*1*___

Tell a brief story, give instructions, or give directions using sequencing words. You may write it in the form of a list or a paragraph. Be sure to use commas when necessary.

_____

_____

_____

_____

_____

_____

_____

Copyright © by Pearson Education, Inc.

GRAMMAR Appositives *Use with textbook page 17.*

> **REMEMBER** An appositive is a noun or noun phrase that renames another noun. An appositive appears near the noun it renames. A nonrestrictive appositive gives extra information about the noun, and a comma is used to set off the appositive. A restrictive appositive gives essential information, and no comma is used.

Underline the appositive in each sentence. Write *R* if the appositive is restrictive or *N* if it is nonrestrictive. Then circle the noun or noun phrase that the appositive renames.

Example: (The clown), <u>a professional entertainer</u>, performed at my party. __*N*__

1. I saw the most magnificent animal, a white-tailed deer, at the park. _____

2. My sister Mary Ellen became a nurse after she graduated. _____

3. St. Petersburg, a city of almost five million people, was designed by Peter the

   Great. _____

4. The U.S. president John Kennedy was known for his speaking skills. _____

5. My brother's car, a red Volkswagen, broke down this morning. _____

6. My friend Bill called me last night. _____

7. A friendly and beautiful tabby, Sam, was my favorite cat. _____

8. My cousin Raymond lives in New Jersey. _____

Copyright © by Pearson Education, Inc.

Complete your own sequence-of-events organizer about an exciting event you participated in or attended.

First

↓

Next

↓

Then

↓

Finally

Use the Peer Review Checklist below to obtain feedback from your partner. This feedback will help you edit your final draft.

PEER REVIEW CHECKLIST

☐ Does the first sentence introduce the main idea?

☐ Is the description organized chronologically?

☐ Did the writer use sequence words to make the sequence clear?

☐ Does the writer include details to make each step of the description vivid?

☐ Does the concluding sentence sum up the experience?

☐ What changes could be made to improve the paragraph?

Copyright © by Pearson Education, Inc.

Name _____ Date _____

VOCABULARY **Key Words** *Use with textbook page 21.*

Write each word in the box next to its definition.

| designer | ~~device~~ | elements | invention | patent | periodic table |

Example: ____*device*____: a machine or other small object that does a special job

1. _____: someone who thinks of ideas for creating something and then draws patterns so they can be made

2. _____: something new that is made for the first time

3. _____: simple chemical substances made of one type of atom

4. _____: a specially arranged list of simple chemical substances

5. _____: a document that says you have the right to make or sell an invention

Use the words in the box at the top of the page to complete the sentences.

6. The class is studying all the known chemical _____.

7. She built a _____ out of some old machine parts in her basement.

8. The engineer applied for a _____ to protect his new

   _____.

9. We made a model from the sketch drawn by the _____.

10. We need to look up a chemical symbol. Do you have a science textbook that shows

    the _____?

Copyright © by Pearson Education, Inc.

Read the paragraph below. Pay attention to the underlined academic words.

> In March 2007, a boat <u>created</u> by a Swiss company made history by sailing across the Atlantic Ocean. The boat had solar panels on its roof whose <u>function</u> was to collect sunlight. This <u>technology</u> allowed the boat to cross the Atlantic using only solar energy. The journey proved that the sun can be a <u>significant</u> source of energy.

Write the letter of the correct definition next to each word.

Example: ___*b*___ function

_____ **1.** significant

_____ **2.** technology

_____ **3.** created

a. made or invented

b. the purpose of something

c. noticeable or important

d. all the knowledge and equipment used in science

Use the academic words from the exercise above to complete the sentences.

4. The machine is very complicated, but its _____ is not clear.

5. New _____ allows people to travel and communicate in new ways.

6. The invention of the printing press was a _____ event.

7. The painter _____ a beautiful new work of art for the gallery.

Complete the sentences with your own ideas.

Example: I think that new technology has made ___*communication much easier*___.

8. One important function of a fence around a yard is to

_____.

9. Once my friends and I created a(n) _____.

10. I spend a significant amount of time on _____.

Copyright © by Pearson Education, Inc.

WORD STUDY — Nouns That Modify Nouns *Use with textbook page 23.*

> **REMEMBER** A noun names a person, place, thing, or idea. Sometimes a noun can function as an adjective to modify (describe) another noun. For example, *piano* is a noun because it names an object. In the phrase *piano music, piano* is an adjective because it modifies the noun *music*. Knowing that a noun can modify a noun helps you use words correctly.

Read each sentence. Then circle the noun modifier and underline the noun being modified.

Example: They ate their (evening) meal.

1. We have a new grocery store in the neighborhood.

2. They sell good breakfast cereal.

3. I like fruit drinks because they are healthful.

4. The package design really gets your attention.

5. You can learn a lot from television advertisements.

Add a noun to modify each noun to complete each sentence.

Example: Charles makes _____*potato*_____ soup

6. Matt got a _____ puppy.

7. Lucille uses too much _____ spray.

8. The _____ towel has a beautiful pattern.

9. Rico buys a _____ ring.

10. The dog likes to chew _____ toys.

Copyright © by Pearson Education, Inc.

Use with textbook page 23.

> **REMEMBER** Recognizing sequence helps you understand the order in which things happen. Look for words that show sequence, such as *first, then, next, finally, last, while, during,* and *after.* Look for dates and times.

Read the paragraph and answer the questions that follow.

Bessie Coleman

On June 15, 1921, Bessie Coleman became the first African-American woman to earn a pilot's license. She got her license in France. Then she returned to the United States and participated in flight shows. In the 1920s, flight shows were one of the few ways that pilots could make a living flying. During this time, Bessie became a figure in the media because she was a woman and an African American who had a pilot's license. She also performed daring stunts.

Although she liked her work and her new-found fame, the next thing she wanted to do was open a flight school for African Americans. Sadly, Bessie died in a plane accident before realizing her dream. But her bravery has inspired many people to pursue their dreams no matter what the obstacles. Today, all Americans can finally pursue their dreams.

1. What is the first event that happens in the passage?

_____

2. What is the next event that happens in the passage?

_____

3. What did Coleman do while she was a pilot?

_____

4. What is the final event described by the passage?

_____

5. How can understanding the order of events help you when reading a story?

_____

Copyright © by Pearson Education, Inc.

COMPREHENSION *Use with textbook page 28.*

Choose the best answer for each item. Circle the letter of the correct answer.

1. Nineteenth-century inventions sped up travel and _____.

   a. traffic   **b.** mathematical calculation   **c.** communication

2. Levi's jeans are named after the man who _____.

   a. provided money to   **b.** made jeans with rivets   **c.** led the California
   gold miners   Gold Rush

3. The first vacuum cleaners were _____.

   a. too big to fit inside   **b.** too small for home use   **c.** so valuable they
   the home   were often stolen

4. The first bubble gum was invented by an _____.

   a. child   **b.** soldier   **c.** accountant

5. "Cat's eyes" make it safer to _____.

   a. fly at night   **b.** swim at night   **c.** drive at night

EXTENSION *Use with textbook page 29.*

Choose five objects that you use today. Research each object to find when and where it was invented. Fill in the chart below.

Object	Origin
pencil	England, 1600s

Copyright © by Pearson Education, Inc.

REMEMBER Form negatives with *did not* (*didn't*) and begin questions with *did*. If the answer to a simple past question is the subject of the sentence, use the affirmative form of the verb.
Example: Who *invented* bubble gum? NOT Who *did invent* bubble gum?

Complete each sentence below with the simple past of the verb in parentheses.

Example: Inventions (transform) _____*transformed*_____ society.

1. My grandmother always (dry) _____ her laundry on a clothesline.

2. We (want) _____ to go swimming, but the pool

   (close) _____ at five.

3. They (try) _____ to invent a new way to communicate.

4. He (not live) _____ in San Francisco for very long before he (move)

   _____.

Complete the following simple past questions with the verb in parentheses. Then answer in complete sentences, using information from the reading.

Example: What ____*did*____ Levi Strauss _____*supply*_____ people with? (supply)
   He supplied them with everything they needed.

5. What _____ Elisha Otis _____? (invent)

   _____

6. What _____ Dimitry Mendeleyev _____ in 1866? (list)

   _____

7. What _____ people to California in the 1850s? (attract)

   _____

8. What _____ Jacob Davis _____ to Levi Strauss? (suggest)

   _____

Copyright © by Pearson Education, Inc.

Name _____ Date _____

REMEMBER The simple past forms of many common verbs are irregular. You must memorize these. The negative of irregular verbs is formed the same way as the negative of regular verbs, with *did not* (*didn't*). Questions begin with *did*. The simple past of the verb *be* is *was* or *were*. The negative is *wasn't* or *weren't*. Questions begin with *was* or *were*.

Complete each sentence below with the simple past of the verb in parentheses.

Example: He (put) _____*put*_____ his jeans in the washing machine.

1. She (know) _____ the answer to the question.

2. There (be) _____ problems with the first transatlantic cable.

3. They (throw) _____ me a surprise birthday party.

4. He (not be) _____ happy about how he (do) _____ on the test.

Complete the following simple past questions with the verb in parentheses. Then answer them in complete sentences, using information from the reading.

Example: What _____*did*_____ people _____*think*_____ was outrageous in the nineteenth century? (think)

   People thought pants for women were outrageous.

5. What _____ Dimitry Mendeleyev _____ about his list of elements? (find out)

   _____

6. What invention _____ bloomers seem like a great idea? (make)

   _____

7. When _____ Davis and Strauss _____ the first patent for jeans? (get)

   _____

8. What _____ Percy Shaw _____ because of his invention? (become)

   _____

Copyright © by Pearson Education, Inc.

Complete your own word web for a paragraph about an object that you have used, eaten, or worn.

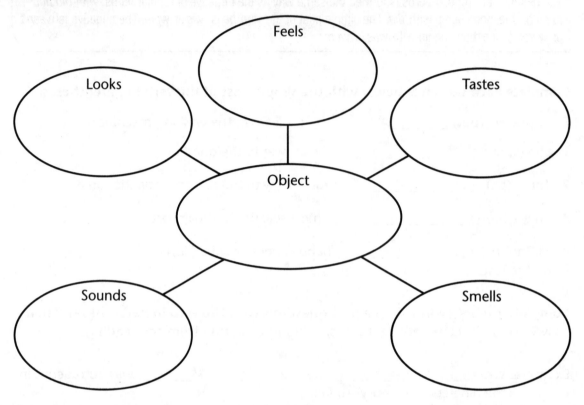

Use the Peer Review Checklist below to obtain feedback from your partner. This feedback will help you edit your final draft.

PEER REVIEW CHECKLIST

☐ Is the main topic of the description clear?

☐ Does the writer include sensory details to describe the object?

☐ Does the paragraph give the reader a vivid picture of the writer's experience?

☐ Does the writer use a variety of verbs and adverbs to make the description vivid?

☐ Are regular and irregular past tense verbs used correctly?

☐ What changes could be made to improve the paragraph?

Copyright © by Pearson Education, Inc.

Name _____ Date _____

How can change improve people's lives?

READING 3: From *Seedfolks*

VOCABULARY **Literary Words** *Use with textbook page 35.*

> **REMEMBER** **Imagery** is descriptive language used in literary works. Imagery is created by using sensory details. **Setting** is the time and place of the action of a story. Sensory details help establish the setting in the reader's mind.

Each sentence establishes its setting or action with sensory details. Label each sentence with the sense it refers to: smell, taste, touch, sight, or sound.

Sense	Description
touch	The hot sand was rough against her feet.
1.	Night had turned the whole town dark gray and black.
2.	The fruit drink was too sugary sweet for me.
3.	The evening breeze brought the faint scent of the autumn leaves through the window.

Read the passage below. Then answer the questions.

> The broad leaves high above us were deep green with hints of yellow and red. Thin beams of light touched the soft ground. Colorful tropical birds called out in strange voices. The dirt below us was moist, and small drops of water fell to the ground. Our guide told us to look up, and we saw two monkeys swinging from a branch. They chattered back and forth like people. The air was warm and sweet.

4. What is the setting of the passage? _____

5. List the sensory details that help establish the setting.

_____

_____

Copyright © by Pearson Education, Inc.

Read the paragraph below. Pay attention to the underlined academic words.

One day my teacher asked our class to come up with a plan to help make our school a more beautiful place. With this <u>goal</u> in mind, I noticed that an old garden bed <u>located</u> next to the parking lot was filled with weeds. In class the next day, I suggested that the class plant a garden there. My teacher and classmates <u>reacted</u> with excitement to my idea. The whole class got <u>involved</u> in planning and planting the new garden.

Write the academic words from the paragraph above next to their correct definition.

Example: _____*located*_____: in a particular place or position

1. _____: included in a project or situation

2. _____: behaved in a particular way because of what someone has said or done

3. _____: something you want to do in the future

Use the academic words from the paragraph above to complete the sentences.

4. Our community garden is _____ on Gonzalez Avenue.

5. Everyone _____ with shock when the news came.

6. She worked all summer to reach her _____.

7. The whole team was _____ in the project.

Complete the sentences with your own ideas.

Example: We learned that many statues are located in _____*Italy*_____.

8. I reacted to the good news by _____.

9. My family likes to get involved in _____.

10. I have a goal this year to _____.

Copyright © by Pearson Education, Inc.

WORD STUDY   Apostrophes *Use with textbook page 37.*

REMEMBER An apostrophe (') is used to show possession with a noun. Add *'s* to the end of a singular noun, such as *book of the girl* ⟶ *girl's book.* Add just the apostrophe to the end of a plural noun, such as *books of the girls* ⟶ *girls' books.* An apostrophe is also used to take the place of missing letters in a contraction. For example, *it* and *is* become the contraction *it's.*

Look at the chart below. Form the possessive of each phrase. Write the possessive in the chart.

Phrase	Possessive Form
the ideas of the boy	*the boy's ideas*
1. the suggestion of Dr. Greene	
2. the toys of the child	
3. the strength of the waves	
4. the laughter of Mona	
5. the petals of the flowers	

Look at the chart below. Form the contraction for each pair of words. Write the contraction in the chart.

Word 1	Word 2	Contraction
I	am	*I'm*
6. you	are	
7. is	not	
8. who	is	
9. they	are	
10. he	will	

Copyright © by Pearson Education, Inc.

> **REMEMBER** When you visualize, you make pictures in your mind of what you are reading.

Read the paragraph and answer the questions that follow.

> I was standing at the edge of the stage, behind the curtain, waiting for my turn in the dance recital. It was an Irish Step dance and I was wearing my step shoes, black tights and a green shirt. Last year, I performed in the recital with a group. But this year, it was just me. My palms felt sweaty. I heard my name announced, and I walked out on stage. There I was, on the stage, by myself. The lights were so bright I couldn't see the audience. For a moment, it felt like no one was there. I kept that thought in my head as I danced. It made it seem as if I were performing for a row of lights, not 200 people. My routine seemed effortless. When I finished I heard applause.

1. What is the passage about?

_____

2. What is the strongest image in the passage?

_____

3. How do the images help you to make a mental picture of the scene?

_____

4. Draw a picture of the scene described in the passage. Be sure to include details from the passage in your drawing.

5. How can the skill of visualizing help you to understand a text more clearly?

_____

Copyright © by Pearson Education, Inc.

COMPREHENSION   *Use with textbook page 44.*

Choose the best answer for each item. Circle the letter of the correct answer.

1. Kim wants to make her father's spirit proud because _____.

   a. he often praised her   **b.** he never knew her   **c.** he was angry with her

2. Kim used the vacant lot to plant _____.

   a. beans   **b.** flowers   **c.** carrots

3. Wendell helps Kim by _____.

   a. giving her advice about when to plant beans   **b.** buying her more beans   **c.** watering the plants

4. Next, Wendell will most likely _____.

   a. plant his own garden   **b.** move out of the area   **c.** talk to Kim about her plants

5. In this story, the neighbors _____.

   a. are afraid of each other   **b.** don't like each other   **c.** look out for each other

RESPONSE TO LITERATURE   *Use with textbook page 45.*

Imagine that you live in the building with Ana, Kim, and Wendell. One day you look out your window and see someone planting flowers in the vacant lot. What do you feel when you see the person? What will you do next? Will you join the person in the garden? Write a short paragraph to describe the situation.

_____

_____

_____

_____

_____

Copyright © by Pearson Education, Inc.

GRAMMAR   **Comparison Structures: Adjectives**

Use with textbook page 46.

> **REMEMBER** A comparative adjective + *than* compares two things. *The* + a superlative adjective
> compares three or more things. For most one-syllable adjectives, form the comparative by adding *-er*
> and the superlative by adding *-est*. For one-syllable adjectives with a consonant-vowel-consonant
> pattern, such as *big*, double the last consonant and add *-er/-est*.
> **Examples:** This math test is *harder* than last week's. That tomato is the *biggest* one in the market.
> For most two-syllable adjectives ending in *-y*, change the *y* to *i* and add *-er* or *-est*.
> **Example:** The *scariest* Halloween was two years ago at my aunt's haunted house.
> Add *more* or *most* before most other adjectives of two or more syllables.
> **Example:** The public pool is *more exciting* than the library.
> Some adjectives have irregular forms.
> **Example:** This is the *worst* dress I have tried on today.

Complete each sentence with the correct form of the adjective in parentheses.

Example: (bright) The stars today are _____ *brighter than* _____ they were
yesterday.

1. (icy) The sidewalk is _____ than the driveway.

2. (serious) He is the _____ student in the class.

3. (good) Broccoli tastes _____ than spinach.

**Write sentences with comparative and superlative adjectives. Follow the directions
in parentheses.**

Example: (Use the superlative form of *large*.)

That is the largest house in the neighborhood.

4. (Use the comparative form of *intelligent*.)

_____

_____

5. (Use the superlative form of *thin*.)

_____

_____

GRAMMAR **Comparison Structures: Adverbs**

Use with textbook page 47.

REMEMBER Use comparative and superlative adverbs to compare two actions. For one-syllable adverbs, add *-er* and *-est* to the adverb. For two- or more syllable adverbs and adverbs that end in *-ly*, use *more* and *most* + adverb. Just as with comparative and superlative adjectives, you can use *than* with comparative adverbs and *the* with superlative adverbs. If the comparison is understood, you don't need the *than* clause.
Example: I am doing better now (than I was before).
Some adverbs are irregular in the comparative and superlative form.
Examples: *well, better, best*; *badly, worse, worst*; and *far, farther* (*further*), *farthest* (*furthest*).
Some adverbs have the same form as adjectives.
Examples: *early, hard, late, fast,* and *high.*
Their comparative and superlative forms are also the same.

Complete each sentence below with the comparative or superlative form of the adverb in parentheses.

Example: I (well) speak English _____*better*_____ now than last year.

1. (politely) She greeted me the _____ out of everyone.

2. (happily) He smiled _____ than before.

3. (badly) Our team played the _____ that we'd ever played.

4. (gracefully) That girl dances the _____ of all.

5. (badly) I have never done _____ than I did on that test.

6. (early) I get up _____ than my brother does.

7. (high) A duck can fly _____ than a chicken can.

8. (hard) Mike works _____ out of anyone in class.

9. (carefully/fast) He drives _____ since he had his

   accident. He drove much _____ in the past.

10. (quietly) We talked _____ after the children went to bed.

Copyright © by Pearson Education, Inc.

Complete your own three-column chart for a paragraph describing a place you are familiar with.

Back	Middle	Front

Use the Peer Review Checklist below to obtain feedback from your partner. This feedback will help you edit your final draft.

PEER REVIEW CHECKLIST

☐ Does the paragraph give an overview of the scene?

☐ Are the parts of the scene described in spatial order?

☐ Is the description organized chronologically?

☐ Does the paragraph give the reader a clear picture of the scene?

☐ Are comparative and superlative adjectives used correctly?

☐ What changes could be made to improve the paragraph?

Copyright © by Pearson Education, Inc.

UNIT 1

How can change improve people's lives?

READING 4: "From Refugees to Fugees"

VOCABULARY **Key Words** *Use with textbook page 51.*

Write each word in the box next to its definition.

athletes	boundaries	professional	responsibilities	sacrifice	uniforms

Example: ___*sacrifice*___ : to give something up

1. _____ : outfits worn by members of a group, such as a sports team

2. _____ : people who are good at sports

3. _____ : things a person has a duty to do

4. _____ : someone who gets paid to do something

5. _____ : the lines that mark the edges of something, such as a playing field

Use the words in the box at the top of the page to complete the sentences.

6. I asked about the _____ of the job when I interviewed.

7. Even though I'm not a _____ artist, I love to draw.

8. She had to _____ a lot to become a skater, but it was worth it.

9. Our new _____ have our team logo.

10. _____ have to practice to be good at their sport.

Copyright © by Pearson Education, Inc.

Read the paragraph below. Pay attention to the underlined academic words.

The "Iditarod" is a famous, 1,161-mile dogsled race across Alaska. The cold weather and extreme length of the race <u>require</u> the racers and the dogs to be in their best physical shape. Good teamwork between man and dog is another important <u>element</u> of a successful dogsled team. The racers must <u>focus</u> on the dogs' performance and safety, and must project a <u>positive</u> attitude until the end. The event is considered one of the last great races of the world.

Write the academic words from the paragraph above next to their correct definitions.

Example: _____*require*_____: need something

1. _____: good or useful

2. _____: one part of a plan, system, piece of writing, and so on

3. _____: give all your attention to a particular person or thing

Use the academic words from the paragraph above to complete the sentences.

4. All his hard work had a _____ effect on his grades.

5. I know that if I _____ on the problem, I can figure it out.

6. Sports like soccer _____ a lot of practice.

7. Sports are an important _____ of my life.

Complete the sentences with your own ideas.

Example: Having a positive approach _*can help you do well at things*_.

8. For me, sports and studying both require _____.

9. This year I will focus on _____.

10. The most interesting element of my current school project is

_____.

Copyright © by Pearson Education, Inc.

WORD STUDY **Spelling Long *a* and *e*** *Use with textbook page 53.*

> **REMEMBER** The long vowel sounds /a/ and /e/ can be spelled several different ways. Long *a* can be spelled *a* as in *labor*, *a_e* as in *make*, *ai* as in *maid*, *ay* as in *day*, and *ea* as in *break*. Long *e* can be spelled *e* as in *he*, *ee* as in *bee*, *ea* as in *pea*, *eo* as in *people*, and *y* as in *lady*.

Read the words in the box below. Then write each word in the correct column in the chart.

clang	evil	create	capacity	leader
afraid	mustang	meow	equal	greater
hay	reader	guarantee	shape	raise
grape	leo	Monday	electricity	agree

/a/ spelled a	/a/ spelled a_e	/a/ spelled ai	/a/ spelled ay	/a/ spelled ea
clang				

/e/ spelled e	/e/ spelled ee	/e/ spelled ea	/e/ spelled eo	/e/ spelled y

Write the letter-sound pattern in each word below.

Example: main *long /a/ spelled ai*

1. scream _____

2. escape _____

3. straight _____

4. Thursday _____

5. sea _____

6. spree _____

Copyright © by Pearson Education, Inc.

> **REMEMBER** Preview the text before reading it by looking at the title, headings, and any visuals. Read the first and last sentences of each paragraph. Ask yourself about the topic to see what you know already. Previewing helps you set a purpose for reading.

Look at the article below and answer the questions that follow.

Mountainous Region of the Western United States of America

Mountain Ranges

The Western United States of America is home to several mountain ranges. They span Colorado to California and Montana to New Mexico. People travel to the mountains to climb, camp and ski. Some visitors go just for the beautiful views and the clear mountain air.

The Sierra Nevada, Cascade and Coastal Ranges spread across the west coast of the United States and into Mexico and Canada.

The Rocky, Sierra Nevada, Cascade and Coastal Ranges

The Rocky Mountain Range spans over 2000 miles from Mexico to Alaska. It is made up of over 100 smaller mountain ranges. The highest peak in the range is near Leadville, Colorado.

1. Read the title and headings. What do you think the article is going to be about?

_____

2. What does the picture tell you about the topic of the article?

_____

3. Read the first and last sentences in each paragraph. What more did you learn about the article?

_____

4. What do you already know about the topic?

_____

5. How can previewing help you understand an article?

_____

Copyright © by Pearson Education, Inc.

COMPREHENSION *Use with textbook page 58.*

Choose the best answers for each item. Circle the letter of the correct answer.

1. Soccer is called "the simplest sport" because _____.

   a. it can only be played in the summer
   b. it requires very little equipment
   c. it doesn't have any official rules

2. Except for the goalie, soccer players can't use their _____.

   a. hands
   b. feet
   c. heads

3. The biggest event in soccer is the _____.

   a. U.S. Open
   b. Super Bowl
   c. World Cup

4. In the United States, soccer is _____.

   a. the most popular sport in the entire country
   b. the fastest-growing team sport
   c. not very popular

5. One special thing about the Fugees team is that _____.

   a. the players are all children of famous players
   b. the players all come from war-torn countries
   c. the players are all members of a famous rock band

EXTENSION *Use with textbook page 59.*

In the United States, two kinds of football are played: American football and soccer. Research to find information about both games. Then use the information to complete the chart below.

	American Football	Soccer
Number of players on the field	11	11
6. Shape of ball		
7. Term for field		
8. Length of game (time)		
9. Name and length of game divisions (time)		
10. Distance between goalposts		

Copyright © by Pearson Education, Inc.

REMEMBER Adjectives give information about people, places, or things. When more than one adjective describes the same noun, the adjectives must be listed in this order: (1) opinion, (2) size, (3) age, (4) shape, (5) color, and (6) material.
Example: Her *beautiful long red* hair is always in her face.

Complete the charts below with adjectives from the box.

a	tall	many	picture	new	confident	imported	cotton	green
rectangular		enormous	old	Asian	oval	~~dark~~	exercise	cheap	rocky

Determiner	Opinion	Size	Age	Shape
a				
			old	

Color	Origin	Material	Purpose
			picture
dark			

Write sentences using the adjectives in parentheses in the correct order before the noun given.

Example: (brick / red / cozy) house *Some day I want a cozy red brick house.*

1. (rocky / dark / small) place

   _____

2. (green / unusual / plastic / square) wastebasket

   _____

3. (leather / black / brand-new / cool) jacket

   _____

4. (old / tall / confident) woman

   _____

5. (brown / young / friendly) dog

   _____

Copyright © by Pearson Education, Inc.

GRAMMAR **Compound Adjectives** *Use with textbook page 61.*

REMEMBER Many compound adjectives are hyphenated. A hyphenated compound adjective usually appears before the noun it modifies.
Hyphenated compound adjectives can be formed by combining an adjective and noun, especially nouns that show time. Notice the noun is singular in the compound adjective.
Examples: He went on vacation for *two weeks.*   He went on a *two-week* vacation.
Hyphenated compound adjectives can also be formed by combining an adjective and noun, using a participial adjective that ends in *-ed.*
Example: She catches with her *left hand.*   She is a *left-handed* catcher.
You can combine a verb and adverb, using a participial adjective that ends in *-ing*, to make a hyphenated compound adjective. Notice the adverb is in adjective form and comes before the participial adjective.
Examples: This glue *dries quickly.*   This is a *quick-drying* glue.

Complete each sentence below with a hyphenated compound adjective using the underlined words.

1. I saw an animal with <u>long legs</u>.

   I saw a _____ animal.

2. He is a student that <u>works hard</u>.

   He is a _____ student.

3. The intermission was <u>fifteen minutes</u>.

   It was a _____ intermission.

4. The movie had a monster with <u>three heads</u>.

   The movie had a _____ monster.

5. We worked with a figure that had <u>six sides</u>.

   We worked with a _____ figure.

6. It was a plane that <u>flew fast</u>.

   It was a _____ plane.

7. I have a bed with <u>four posts</u>.

   I have a _____ bed.

8. The cake had <u>three layers</u>.

   It was a _____ cake.

Copyright © by Pearson Education, Inc.

Complete your own T-chart about a group of people.

Group	
Trait	**Example**

Use the Peer Review Checklist below to obtain feedback from your partner. This feedback will help you edit your final draft.

PEER REVIEW CHECKLIST

- ☐ Does the first sentence introduce the main idea?
- ☐ Does the paragraph describe the group's main characteristics?
- ☐ Does the writer use a variety of adjectives to support the description?
- ☐ Does the paragraph include details that develop the description?
- ☐ Does the paragraph give a clear understanding of the special characteristics of the group?
- ☐ What changes could be made to improve the paragraph?

Copyright © by Pearson Education, Inc.

WRITING WORKSHOP   *Use with textbook pages 68–71.*

Organize your ideas in the graphic organizer below.

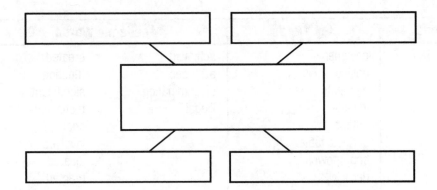

Use the Peer Review Checklist below to obtain feedback from your partner. This feedback will help you edit your final draft.

PEER REVIEW CHECKLIST

☐ Does the first paragraph introduce the topic?

☐ Does the concluding paragraph sum up the main ideas?

☐ Does the essay describe the experience clearly?

☐ Is the description organized chronologically?

☐ Is there a development in the writer's feelings before and after the experience?

☐ Is it clear why the experience changed the writer?

☐ What changes could be made to improve the essay?

Copyright © by Pearson Education, Inc.

Underline the vocabulary items you know and can use well. Review and practice any you haven't underlined. Underline them when you know them well.

Literary Words	Key Words	Academic Words	
plot	designer	achieved	created
conflict	device	attitudes	function
imagery	elements	discrimination	significant
setting	invention	illegal	technology
	patent		goal
	periodic table		involved
	boom towns		located
	derrick		reacted
	employment		affects
	gusher		available
	headquarters		environment
	wound		region

Put a check by the skills you can perform well. Review and practice any you haven't checked off. Check them off when you can perform them well.

Skills	I can . . .
Word Study	☐ recognize and spell double consonants. ☐ recognize and use nouns modifying nouns. ☐ use apostrophes. ☐ spell and pronounce long *a* and *e*.
Reading Strategies	☐ analyze historical context. ☐ recognize sequence. ☐ visualize. ☐ preview.
Grammar	☐ use sequence words and appositives. ☐ use regular and irregular simple past verbs. ☐ use comparison structures. ☐ use correct adjective order and compound adjectives.
Writing	☐ describe an event or experience. ☐ describe an object. ☐ describe a place. ☐ write a descriptive essay. ☐ describe a group of people.

Copyright © by Pearson Education, Inc.

Test Preparation

TEST 1

DIRECTIONS
Read this selection. Then answer the questions that follow it.

Jing and Sarah are in Mrs. Sampson's class. They have to do a report about where refugees settle in the United States. Jing is very excited when he finds this chart. He thinks it will help them for the report.

Refugee Settlement in 2009

State	Rank	Number of Refugees
Arizona	4	4,320
California	1	11,278
Florida	5	4,193
Michigan	6	3,500
New York	3	4,412
Texas	2	8,212

1 Which state receives the most refugees?

   A   Arizona

   B   Califonia

   C   New York

   D   Texas

2 Which state is ranked third?

   F   Texas

   G   Michigan

   H   Florida

   J   New York

3 Who wants Sarah to do a report?

   A   Jing

   B   Her father

   C   The class

   D   Mrs. Sampson

Copyright © by Pearson Education, Inc.

DIRECTIONS
Read this selection. Then answer the questions that follow it.

Hubble Space Telescope

1   Edwin Hubble was an astronomer—a scientist who studied objects in space. Hubble saw that galaxies were moving away from Earth. He guessed that the universe is getting bigger. He formulated a law called Hubble's Law based on this discovery. The Hubble Space Telescope is also named for him.

2   The Hubble Space Telescope was designed in 1970, but it was not launched until 1990. The telescope was launched from the space shuttle Discovery. The telescope orbits Earth and takes pictures, moving at a speed of five miles per second. It completes a journey around the Earth every ninety-seven minutes!

3   The pictures that the Hubble Space Telescope sends back to Earth provide scientists with a clear view of our solar system. In addition, the telescope allows astronomers to see images of many different galaxies.

4   The telescope was designed with the idea that it could be <u>upgraded</u>, or made better, while it was still in orbit. The National Aeronautics and Space Administration (NASA) sends astronauts to service the telescope. They fix problems, replace equipment, and add new equipment. Astronauts have serviced the telescope five times since it was first launched. The last servicing mission was in May 2009.

---

1 According to the selection, how does the Hubble Space Telescope help scientists?

  A It can be upgraded with new technology.

  B It proves Hubble's Law is true.

  C It gives astronauts a chance to visit the telescope.

  D It gives scientists a clear picture of the solar system.

2 What is paragraph 4 mainly about?

  F Servicing the telescope

  G New technology added to the telescope

  H Problems with the telescope

  J The last servicing mission

3 Which words in paragraph 4 help the reader know what *upgraded* means?

  A in orbit

  B made better

  C was designed

  D the idea

4 The author probably wrote this selection to —

  F compare the Hubble Space Telescope to other telescopes

  G encourage people to find out more about the Hubble Space Telescope

  H explain what the Hubble Space Telescope is and what it does

  J describe the pictures the Hubble Space Telescope sends to scientists

Copyright © by Pearson Education, Inc.

TEST 3

DIRECTIONS
Read this selection. Then answer the questions that follow it.

Lee's Lesson

1 Lee looked forward to Saturdays because that was the day he visited his grandmother. Each Saturday Lee and his family drove to Houston, where they visited his grandmother at her restaurant in Chinatown. During the day they would help Mei in the kitchen or with customers. In the evening they would eat some of her delicious dumplings and listen to her stories.

2 This Saturday was no different. After their meal, Mei sat in her favorite chair. Lee sat beside her. "Have I told you the story of the ruler who wanted to understand the world?" she asked.

3 "No, you haven't," Lee replied. So Mei began her story.

4 The ruler asked his adviser if it was possible to understand the world. In reply, the adviser told the following story:

5 One day, three men were walking together in the forest. They challenged each other to a game. Each man put a blindfold over his eyes.

6 The men encountered an elephant sleeping in the woods. "What is this thing?" wondered the first man. He reached out and touched one of the elephant's legs and said, "This feels rough and thick, and my arms barely go around it. Surely, this is a tree."

7 The second man laughed. "No, you're wrong, my friend," he replied from his position by the elephant's trunk. "My fingers go around it, and it is <u>flexible</u>. See? It can be easily bent. It is a snake."

8 "Silly friends, you're both wrong," responded the third man. He was standing at the elephant's side and touching the elephant's stomach. "This is a long, wide wall," he said. "I'm sure of it."

9 After the story, the adviser turned to the ruler. "So, Sire," concluded the adviser, "think of this story the next time you believe anyone's story about an event."

10 After Mei finished her story, Lee and his family said good-bye and drove home. Lee thought about his grandmother's story. He wondered if the ruler had learned the same lesson he had.

Copyright © by Pearson Education, Inc.

1 Use this story map to answer the question below.

Event 1	Event 2	Event 3	Outcome
Lee and his family visit his grandmother.	Lee and his family help his grandmother at her restaurant.	Mei tells Lee a story about a ruler who wants to understand the world.	

Which of these belongs in the empty box in the story map?

A Lee learns a lesson from his grandmother's story.

B Lee and his family stay at Mei's house.

C The three men tell what they think the elephant is.

D The ruler in the story learns a lesson.

2 Paragraph 1 is mainly about —

F Mei's restaurant and her stories

G Lee and his family

H why Lee enjoys visiting his grandmother

J Mei's delicious dumplings

3 In paragraph 7, what words help the reader know what <u>flexible</u> means?

A go around it

B a snake

C easily bent

D my fingers

4 Which sentence from the story shows how Lee feels about his grandmother?

F *In the evening they would eat some of her delicious dumplings and listen to her stories.*

G *Lee looked forward to Saturdays because that was the day he visited his grandmother.*

H *During the day they would help Mei in the kitchen or with customers.*

J *Lee thought about his grandmother's story.*

5 By the end of the story, the reader can conclude that Lee —

A learned a lesson about helping his grandmother

B learned that helping your family is important to success

C learned that his grandmother's stories could be funny

D learned the importance of finding out about the world for yourself

Copyright © by Pearson Education, Inc.

Visual Literacy: Smithsonian American
Art Museum *Use with textbook pages 74–75*

LEARNING TO LOOK

Look at *Storm King on the Hudson* by Samuel Colman on page 75 in your textbook. Place a blank sheet of paper over the right half of the painting. Write down three details that you see on the left side of the painting. State facts, not opinions.

Left Side

Example: _There is smoke from the steamship._ _____

1. _____

_____

2. _____

_____

3. _____

_____

Now move the blank sheet of paper over to cover the left half of the painting. Write down three details that you see on the right side of the painting. State facts, not opinions.

Right Side

4. _____

_____

5. _____

_____

6. _____

_____

Copyright © by Pearson Education, Inc.

Look at *Storm King on the Hudson* again. Imagine a day in the life of the men in the fishing boat on the right side of the painting. What would their day be like? Write your answers below.

Men in Fishing Boat

Example: _It is very hot out here._

_____

_____

_____

Now imagine a day in the life of the men on the steamship on the left side of the painting. What would their day be like? Write your answers below.

Men in Steamship

_____

_____

_____

5W&H

Look at *Fermented Soil* by Hans Hofmann on page 74 in your textbook. Write six questions you would like to ask the artist about this painting.

Example: _What color did you use first?_

1. Who _____

2. Where _____

3. When _____

4. What _____

5. Why _____

6. How _____

Copyright © by Pearson Education, Inc.

Name _____ Date _____

What are the benefits of facing challenges?

READING 1: "The Train to Freedom" / "Follow the Drinking Gourd"

VOCABULARY Key Words *Use with textbook page 79.*

Write each word in the box next to its definition.

| fugitive | heritage | network | ~~runaway~~ | shelter | Underground Railroad |

Example: ___*runaway*___: someone who has left home or the place where he/she is supposed to be

1. _____: group of people or organizations that are connected or that work together

2. _____: a network of people who helped slaves escape to freedom during the 1800s

3. _____: someone trying to avoid being caught, especially by the police

4. _____: the traditional beliefs, values, and customs of a family, group, or country

5. _____: protection from weather or danger

Use the words in the box at the top of the page to complete the sentences.

6. The police searched everywhere for the _____ who had escaped from jail.

7. We looked for _____ when it started to rain.

8. My friend learned that in 1856, members of his family escaped slavery through the

   _____.

9. The _____ enslaved man sneaked out of the slave master's home in the early hours of the morning.

10. When Amy lost her dog, Max, a _____ of friends helped her find him.

Copyright © by Pearson Education, Inc.

Read the paragraph below. Pay attention to the underlined academic words.

During World War II, the United States military wanted to create a <u>code</u> that could not be broken by the enemy. This was a great <u>challenge</u>. The military finally decided to base the code on the language spoken by a Native American tribe, the Navajo. In May of 1942, the first 29 Navajo men came to <u>aid</u> the military. After they helped develop the code, they <u>accompanied</u> the soldiers overseas to help send and receive the secret messages.

Write the letter of the correct definition next to each word.

Example: ___*d*___ accompanied

_____ **1.** aid

_____ **2.** code

_____ **3.** challenge

a. help or support given to someone

b. a way to use words, letters, or numbers to send secret messages

c. something difficult that you need skill or ability to do

d. went somewhere with someone

Use the academic words from the exercise above to complete the sentences.

4. My aunt _____ my class on a school trip.

5. Alex and his sister used a secret _____ to pass messages.

6. We expected an easy math test, but it was a major _____.

7. The teacher offered _____ to the students who were falling behind by helping them after class.

Complete the sentences with your own ideas.

Example: My ___*best friend*___ accompanied me to the park.

8. When I need help, _____ can offer me aid.

9. _____ sends messages in code.

10. I think the biggest challenge I face is _____.

Copyright © by Pearson Education, Inc.

WORD STUDY **Words with *ch* and *tch*** *Use with textbook page 81.*

REMEMBER In English, the consonant clusters *ch* and *tch* sound the same but are spelled differently. For example: *touch* and *match*. Learning these two patterns can help you spell many words correctly.

Read the words in the box below. Then write each word in the correct column in the chart.

chain	switch	attach	sketch	latch
such	watch	touch	patch	champion

Words with *-ch*	Words with *-tch*
chain	

Fill in the missing letters in each word. Use *ch* or *tch*. Check your answers in a dictionary.

Example: Mark shouldn't scra__*tch*__ his mosquito bite!

1. Cleaning my room is one of my _____ores.

2. I have to do some resear_____ on chimpanzees.

3. Risa has one _____apter left to read in the novel.

4. On Saturday, I baked a ba_____ of cookies.

5. My favorite vegetables are carrots, peas, and spina_____.

6. We usually stre_____ before and after we exercise.

Copyright © by Pearson Education, Inc.

REMEMBER You can skim a text to help you get a general understanding of what it is about before you read it more carefully.

Skim the paragraphs below. Answer the questions that follow.

Start Your Day with Breakfast

Breakfast is a great way to start your day because it provides energy for moving and thinking. After being inactive and sleeping for eight hours, breakfast provides you with the energy to get your day started. When you eat breakfast, your stomach breaks down food into nutrients. Your brain needs nutrients to think faster and more clearly, and your body needs them in order to be active.

Scientific research also shows that breakfast is good for your body. Researchers have found that people who skip the first meal of the day end up eating more later, which can lead to weight gain. Studies have also shown that people who eat breakfast on a regular basis have good cholesterol levels and live longer. So slow down, if only for a minute, and have something to eat before you leave your house in the morning.

---

1. What is the first paragraph about?

   _____

2. Read the first sentence of the next paragraph. What do you think it will be about?

   _____

3. Skim the rest of the text. Then, summarize the entire passage in one sentence.

   _____

4. What might you learn from this passage? Set a purpose for reading the passage.

   _____

5. How might skimming a passage before reading it help you to better understand the text?

   _____

Copyright © by Pearson Education, Inc.

COMPREHENSION   *Use with textbook page 88.*

Choose the best answer for each item. Circle the letter of the correct answer.

1. The Underground Railroad was _____.

   a. a network of people   **b.** a network of secret   **c.** a network of tunnels
                                      railroad lines

2. Harriet Tubman was nicknamed "Moses," after _____.

   a. a Biblical figure   **b.** an abolitionist leader   **c.** Union spy

3. To escape from slavery was _____.

   a. something no one   **b.** not a challenge   **c.** difficult and dangerous
        tried to do

4. Slavery was widespread _____.

   a. only in the South   **b.** in both the North   **c.** mainly in other countries
                                      and South

5. Runaway slaves communicated with the Underground Railroad _____.

   a. by telegram   **b.** by telephone   **c.** in secret codes

EXTENSION   *Use with textbook page 89.*

Think of a difficult challenge that you have faced. Was there someone who helped you overcome it? This person might have been a hero to you, like Harriet Tubman was to many runaway slaves. Write a few sentences about the challenge. Then write a thank you note to the person who helped you.

_____

_____

_____

_____

_____

_____

_____

Copyright © by Pearson Education, Inc.

REMEMBER Prepositions such as *at* and *in* can be used to show time; they answer *When?*
In, *to*, and *from* can be used to show place; they answer *Where?*
By, *with*, *from*, *for*, and *of* can be used to provide details; they answer *How?* or *Why?*
A preposition is always followed by a noun or noun phrase. This is called a prepositional phrase.

Underline the prepositional phrase in each sentence. Then write the question that each answers: *When? Where? How?* or *Why?*

Example: The team scored another point <u>by stealing the ball</u>. _____*How?*_____

1. He got to school at 8:45. _____

2. The old man rose slowly from the chair. _____

3. I was calling with my cell phone. _____

4. The doors were locked with a deadbolt. _____

5. He spoke softly into the phone. _____

Complete each sentence with one of the prepositions from the box.

in	to	from	for	of	at

Example: He lived _____*in*_____ New York for many years.

6. Several _____ the people had left.

7. He left the office _____ five o'clock.

8. We learned English _____ a native speaker.

9. They are going _____ Berlin this summer.

10. My father worked _____ the Peace Corps when he was young.

Copyright © by Pearson Education, Inc.

GRAMMAR **Present and Past Progressive** *Use with textbook page 91.*

> **REMEMBER** The present progressive shows an action in progress now or in the future. Form the present progressive with *is*, *am*, or *are* and a present participle. The past progressive shows an action in progress at some time in the past. Form the past progressive with *was* or *were* and the present participle. To show that the action was interrupted, use the simple past with the past progressive. The adverb *while* with the clause in the present progressive implies a duration of time; the adverb *when* with the clause in the simple past implies a point in time.

Underline the verb(s) in each sentence. Write whether the action is in the *present*, *past*, or *future*.

Example: <u>I'm going</u> to Morocco on vacation this summer. _____*future*_____

1. I was taking a bath when the phone rang. _____

2. She's cooking dinner right now. _____

3. We're staying at a hotel next weekend. _____

4. At 5:30, I was washing the dishes. _____

Complete each sentence below with the present progressive, past progressive, or simple past of the verb in parentheses.

Example: He's_*working*_____ (work) on his project this afternoon.

5. What _____ you _____ (do) after work today?

6. What _____ you _____ (do) when I

_____ (call) you yesterday?

7. I can't talk right now. I _____ (shop) for some presents.

8. She _____ (not watch) the movie last night. She

_____ (cooking) instead.

Copyright © by Pearson Education, Inc.

Complete your own word web with details for a fictional narrative beginning with the story starter: *The view was unlike anything I had ever seen before.*

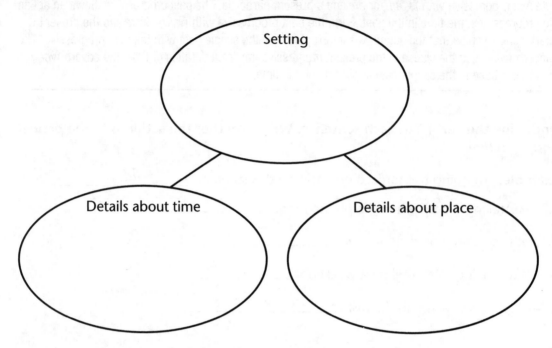

Setting

Details about time

Details about place

Use the Peer Review Checklist below to obtain feedback from your partner. This feedback will help you edit your final draft.

PEER REVIEW CHECKLIST

☐ Does the paragraph have a clear setting?

☐ Is the setting specific and believable?

☐ Does the writer describe the place and the time?

☐ Is the paragraph an interesting story starter? Does it make you want to read more?

☐ Are prepositions used correctly?

☐ Are present and past progressive tenses used correctly?

☐ What changes could be made to improve the paragraph?

Copyright © by Pearson Education, Inc.

UNIT 2 What are the benefits of facing challenges?

READING 2: "Five New Words at a Time" / "Quilt"

VOCABULARY **Literary Words** *Use with textbook page 95.*

REMEMBER **Characters** are the people or animals involved in a story. Stories are told from the **point of view** of a character or narrator. When you are reading a story, it is important to know who is telling the story. The story is told from that character's point of view. Words such as *I, our,* and *us* normally indicate a *first-person* point of view. An author's memoirs or diaries use the first-person point of view. Words such as *he, she,* and *they* normally indicate a *third-person* point of view. If someone who isn't in the story is telling it, the third-person point of view is used.

Label each sentence with the point of view that is used. Write the name of the character.

Point of View / Character	Sentence
third person / Norman	Norman went to the party.
1.	"Are we going?" my friend asked.
2.	"I'm tired, too," I replied.
3.	We sat down and tried to think of an answer.

Write a sentence for each character and point of view.

Character / Point of View	Sentence
Meredith: first person	*I sang the song with a smile.*
4. Samuel: third person	
5. the team: first person	

Copyright © by Pearson Education, Inc.

Read the paragraph below. Pay attention to the underlined academic words.

> Maria is my French pen pal. We <u>communicate</u> mainly through e-mail. I write to her in French, and she writes to me in English. It's exciting when I get a <u>response</u> from her. We <u>approach</u> learning a foreign language in similar ways. We both like reading and writing, and we also enjoy using <u>resources</u> such as language CDs and videos to help with listening and pronunciation.

Write the academic words from the paragraph above next to their correct definitions.

Example: _____*response*_____: something that is said, written, or done as a reaction or reply to something else

1. _____: a supply of materials used to complete a task

2. _____: express your thoughts or feelings so other people understand them

3. _____: a way of doing something or dealing with a problem

Use the academic words from the paragraph above to complete the sentences.

4. The _____ to your letter can be found in today's newspaper.

5. Yu-Lan always used school _____, such as the library and computers.

6. I usually _____ by e-mail with my friend in Germany.

7. We tried a new _____ to solve the problem.

Complete the sentences with your own ideas.

Example: I approach tough projects ___*slowly and carefully*___.

8. I got a positive response when I asked my friends to

_____.

9. I communicate with friends by _____.

10. Some useful resources in my town are _____.

Copyright © by Pearson Education, Inc.

WORD STUDY   Prefixes *im-, over-, un-, after-*

Use with textbook page 97.

> **REMEMBER** A prefix is a letter or group of letters added to the beginning of a word to change its meaning. For example, the prefixes *im-* and *un-* mean "not." When you add *im-* to the word *possible*, the new word is *impossible*, the opposite of *possible*. Knowing just a few prefixes can help you figure out many unfamiliar words.

Look at the chart below. Add the prefixes *im-, over-, un-,* or *after-* as directed to create a new word. Write the new word on the chart. Then write the meaning.

Base Word	Prefix	New Word	Definition
balance	im-	imbalance	not balanced
1. patient	im-		
2. estimate	over-		
3. flow	over-		
4. even	un-		
5. healthy	un-		
6. thought	after-		
7. shock	after-		

Create a new word by adding the prefix *im-, over-, un-,* or *after-* to each word below. Write the definition next to the new word. Check a dictionary if needed.

Example: heat ___overheat   heat to excess_____

 8. taste _____

 9. steady _____

10. effect _____

11. measurable _____

12. pay _____

13. believable _____

14. mature _____

15. look _____

Copyright © by Pearson Education, Inc.

Use with textbook page 97.

REMEMBER When you find the problems and solutions in a text, you will understand it better.

Read the paragraph and answer the questions that follow.

Hannah could see that her dog, Fergus, was thirsty and hot from running in the summer sun, but she'd forgotten to bring water. She was warned that he might get overheated. Hannah made Fergus lie down, but that didn't help. Then she remembered there was a creek at the edge of the park. She took Fergus to the creek where he could get a drink of water.

1. What is the problem in the passage?

   _____

2. What is the solution in the passage?

   _____

Read the paragraph and answer the questions that follow.

Supunnee missed her friends in Thailand, and she wouldn't be going home again for several months. She wondered what her friends were doing, and she felt sad. Then she remembered the friendly girl, Caroline, whom she'd met in class. She decided to give her a call. They made plans to meet before class for lunch. Supunnee felt much better.

3. What is the problem in the passage?

   _____

4. What is the solution in the passage?

   _____

5. How might the skill of identifying problems and solutions help you when reading a story or informational text?

   _____

Copyright © by Pearson Education, Inc.

COMPREHENSION   *Use with textbook page 102.*

Choose the best answer for each item. Circle the letter of the correct answer.

1. Yu-Lan dreaded going to school because _____.

   a. she was the smallest student

   b. she was afraid of not understanding people

   c. her mother's bad English embarrassed her

2. Yu-Lan's mother worked in a Chinese-speaking restaurant because _____.

   a. she wanted to cook Chinese food

   b. she wanted to work during the night instead of the day

   c. she didn't know much English

3. When Yu-Lan was upset, her mother _____.

   a. was cruel to her

   b. gave her confidence

   c. did not understand

4. Yu-Lan and her mother practiced English by _____.

   a. reading together

   b. going to classes together

   c. speaking English at the restaurant

5. "Quilt" is about the way families _____.

   a. seem brand-new and well put-together

   b. fall apart after many years

   c. stay together even in hard times

RESPONSE to LITERATURE   *Use with textbook page 103.*

In the poem "Quilt," Janet Wong compares the connections between her family members to the threads and fabric in a quilt. The quilt is a symbol of the love in her family. Think about your own family and friends. Write a short paragraph about a symbol that best represents the connections between you and the people you love.

_____

_____

_____

_____

_____

_____

Copyright © by Pearson Education, Inc.

GRAMMAR **Gerunds as Subjects and Subject Complements**

Use with textbook page 104.

> **REMEMBER** A gerund is the *-ing* form of a verb that can function as a noun. When a gerund or gerund phrase is the subject of a sentence, it is followed by a third-person-singular verb. When a gerund is a subject complement, it follows a linking verb, such as *be*. To form a negative gerund, use *not* before the gerund.
> **Example:** *Memorizing the words* is helpful, but my mistake is *not being thorough.*

Complete the sentences with the gerund form of the verbs from the box.

not drink	~~surprise~~	see	bake	wash	walk

Example: _____*Surprising*_____ someone on his or her birthday is fun.

1. _____ enough water when it's hot is a bad idea.

2. A good form of exercise is _____.

3. _____ a live performance is always exciting.

4. The best way to spend a rainy day is _____ cookies.

5. His least favorite chore at home is _____ the dishes.

Write sentences about yourself with gerunds as subjects or subject complements, using the verbs in parentheses.

Example: (drive) _*Driving long distances makes me sleepy.*_

6. (win) _____

_____

7. (travel) _____

_____

8. (give) _____

_____

Copyright © by Pearson Education, Inc.

GRAMMAR **Gerunds as Objects** *Use with textbook page 105.*

REMEMBER A gerund or gerund phrase can be the object of certain verbs, such as *appreciate*, *start*, *mention*, or *mind*. A gerund or gerund phrase can also be the object of a preposition or certain verb-preposition combinations, such as *participate in*, *talk about*, and *insist on*.

Complete the sentences with the gerund form of the verbs from the box.

| explain | say | ~~go~~ | eat | meet | run | stand | change |

Example: You should keep _____*going*_____ until you see a stop sign.

1. He has a habit of _____ funny things.

2. The teacher did not bother _____ the answers.

3. I tried _____ on one leg for ten minutes.

4. He began _____ in races when he was fifteen.

5. Did you stop _____ meat?

6. Sammy avoided _____ Jane after their date.

7. I'm considering _____ my major from biology to English.

Write sentences about yourself with gerunds as objects, using the verbs in parentheses.

Example: (cook) *I love cooking a big pot of soup on cold days.* _____

8. (write)

_____

9. (research)

_____

10. (bike)

_____

Copyright © by Pearson Education, Inc.

Complete your own T-chart comparing different characters' points of view from a story you know well.

Use the Peer Review Checklist below to obtain feedback from your partner. This feedback will help you edit your final draft.

PEER REVIEW CHECKLIST

☐ Does the paragraph help the reader to understand the character's point of view?

☐ Does the paragraph describe the feelings and opinions of the character?

☐ Is the character interesting? Is it well developed?

☐ Are pronouns used correctly?

☐ Are gerunds used as subjects, subject complements, and objects?

☐ What changes could be made to improve the paragraph?

Copyright © by Pearson Education, Inc.

Name _____ Date _____

What are the benefits of facing challenges?

READING 3: "An Interview with Gary Paulsen" / From *Hatchet*

VOCABULARY   **Literary Words** *Use with textbook page 109.*

REMEMBER An **author's influences** are factors that may affect his or her writing. These include personal experiences, culture, and world events. An **external conflict** is a struggle between a character and some kind of outside force. This can be another person or a force of nature.

Read each sentence. Write *yes* **if it depicts an external conflict. Write** *no* **if it does not depict an external conflict.**

External?	Description
no	Tom wanted a cup of coffee very badly.
1.	Paolo struggled to cross the stream without falling.
2.	She didn't think she could get past the mean guard dog.
3.	I woke up angry today.
4.	Agi's father always tells her what to do.
5.	The rain made us all wet and cold.

Read the brief author interview below. Circle the author influences that are discussed in the interview.

Q: Have your experiences affected your writing at all?

A: Yes, I moved to Chicago from rural Ohio when I was twenty. The move was difficult for me, but I came to love the city. My favorite setting for my stories is Chicago, and my characters often struggle with the hardships of city life. It is easy to meet people in the city, and I had many good friends who helped me. Often my characters will find someone who similarly helps them. The lessons I have learned from people I admire are more important to me than writing about favorite places or things.

Copyright © by Pearson Education, Inc.

Read the paragraph below. Pay attention to the underlined academic words.

> The rivers of the northwestern United States are home to millions of salmon. Salmon need to travel up and down the rivers to <u>survive</u>. Unfortunately, many of these rivers are blocked by dams. Each <u>structure</u> creates lakes and helps make fresh water <u>available</u> to humans. However, the dams also block the salmon's path and have <u>injured</u> or killed many salmon as they try to pass through them.

Write the academic words from the paragraph above next to their correct definitions.

Example: ___*available*___ : able to be used or seen

1. _____: continue to live after an accident or illness

2. _____: hurt

3. _____: a building or something that has been built

Use the academic words from the paragraph above to complete the sentences.

4. We were surprised that no one was _____ in the crash.

5. I'm not _____ to talk during lunchtime.

6. If you were lost in the woods, would it be possible to _____ on water and berries?

7. Turn right at the giant steel _____ being built in the middle of town.

Complete the sentences with your own ideas.

Example: I want to survive to the age of _____ *250* _____.

8. The _____ is a famous structure in our town.

9. In our school library, _____ are available as resources to help students learn.

10. If you're not careful, you can get injured while _____.

Copyright © by Pearson Education, Inc.

WORD STUDY **Closed Compound Nouns** *Use with textbook page 111.*

REMEMBER A compound noun is made up of two or more nouns. Compound nouns can be written in different ways. A closed compound noun is written as one word, as in *sailboat*.

Look at the nouns in the boxes below. Then combine the nouns in each row to make a closed compound noun.

Noun	+ Noun	= Compound Noun
stock	broker	*stockbroker*
1. sales	person	
2. data	base	
3. tooth	paste	
4. black	board	
5. sea	port	

Create closed compound nouns by combining the nouns in the box. Then use each closed compound noun in a sentence. Note that nouns may be used more than once.

burn	bed	coat	room	beam	drop	rain	fall	sun	dial

Example: _bed + room = bedroom   We painted the bedroom white._

6. _____

7. _____

8. _____

9. _____

10. _____

Copyright © by Pearson Education, Inc.

REMEMBER Before you read, predict what a story will be about. You can also make new predictions as you read. Stop from time to time and ask, "What will happen next?" Look for clues in the story. Think about what you already know.

Read the paragraph and answer the questions that follow.

Seeing Stefan Again

One Saturday morning Angela and her two cousins were riding the subway downtown to the New York Public Library to do research. Two stops before they were going to get off, Angela saw Stefan waiting on a subway platform. She shouted "Stefan!" just before the subway doors closed. He turned just in time to see her before the train left the stop. When they reached the public library stop, Angela got off the train and stood on the platform, stunned she had seen him in the city. She was still standing there when the next train arrived and Stefan stepped through the sliding doors.

1. Read the title. What do you predict the story will be about?

_____

2. Where does the story happen?

_____

3. When does the story happen?

_____

4. After you read the paragraph, what do you predict will happen next?

_____

5. Set a purpose for reading this text.

_____

Copyright © by Pearson Education, Inc.

COMPREHENSION *Use with textbook page 120.*

Choose the best answer for each item. Circle the letter of the correct answer.

1. Gary Paulsen's childhood was _____.

   a. difficult for him   **b.** boring for him   **c.** enjoyable for him

2. As an adult, Paulsen has reacted to his childhood by _____.

   a. trying to forget it   **b.** writing about it   **c.** going back to where
                                                                     he grew up

3. Brian, the character in *Hatchet*, is _____.

   a. like the author,   **b.** not like the author,   **c.** a pilot in Canada
      Gary Paulsen   Gary Paulsen

4. Brian is a(n) _____.

   a. mean person   **b.** scared person   **c.** adventuresome person

5. Gary Paulsen says the best thing for young writers is to _____.

   a. write alone   **b.** only read poetry   **c.** read all the time

RESPONSE TO LITERATURE *Use with textbook page 121.*

Gary Paulsen drew on his own childhood to create the story *Hatchet*. Find a paragraph or image that you like very much in *Hatchet*. Draw a picture illustrating the paragraph or image.

Copyright © by Pearson Education, Inc.

Use with textbook page 122.

> **REMEMBER** A simple sentence contains a subject and a predicate. The predicate tells what the subject does. A predicate always has a verb. **Example:** I walk my dog after school.
> A compound sentence has two simple sentences joined by a coordinating conjunction (*and, but,* or *so*), so it often has two verbs. Use a comma before the conjunction that joins the two sentences.
> **Example:** I swim after school, and sometimes I play soccer.
> Remember that *and* connects two ideas, *but* contrasts two ideas, and *so* shows a result.

Write *simple* if a sentence is simple. Write *compound* if it is compound.

_____ 1. Birds and butterflies fly south in the fall.

_____ 2. The sun rises in the east, and it sets in the west.

_____ 3. Spending time in the woods and by the ocean teaches you about nature.

_____ 4. Dragonflies migrate but they fly in only one direction.

_____ 5. I became interested in Gary Paulsen, so now I want to read more of his books.

Write compound sentences by adding the coordinating conjunction in parentheses and a simple sentence.

Example: (and) Bees were buzzing, _and in the distance a crow was cawing._

6. (but) They planted a garden, _____

7. (and) She went for a walk in the woods, _____

8. (so) Tomorrow he will build a tree house, _____

9. (so) It was getting cold, _____

10. (but) It has not rained all week, _____

Copyright © by Pearson Education, Inc.

GRAMMAR   Agreement in Simple and Compound Sentences

Use with textbook page 123.

REMEMBER In simple sentences and in both independent clauses in compound sentences, the verbs must agree in number with their subjects. For example, if the subject is a plural noun or pronoun (*the boys*, *them*, etc.), the verb must be plural (*take*, *were*, etc.). Pronouns must agree with their antecedent, which is the noun that precedes the pronouns that refer to it. For example, if the antecedent is singular and feminine (*the girl*, *Anna*, etc.), the pronouns that follow must be singular and feminine (*she*, *hers*, etc.).

Rewrite the sentences, correcting the errors in verb agreement and antecedent-pronoun agreement.

Example: The boys has finished my homework.

The boys have finished their homework.

1. Our teacher don't like noisy students. She make him leave class.

_____

2. The pony haven't eaten today, and they are hungry.

_____

3. My head hurt, so she took some medicine.

_____

4. Ben go to a private school, but her sister go to a public school.

_____

5. We doesn't have a new car, but they is good enough for me.

_____

6. The television were broken, so I played a game.

_____

Copyright © by Pearson Education, Inc.

Complete a graphic organizer for a letter to a friend or relative about a memorable event you've experienced.

Use the Peer Review Checklist below to obtain feedback from your partner. This feedback will help you edit your final draft.

PEER REVIEW CHECKLIST

☐ Are all five parts of the letter included?
☐ Does the paragraph describe a detailed sequence of events?
☐ Are the events presented in chronological order?
☐ Does the paragraph include vivid sensory details?
☐ Does the paragraph use simple and compound sentences with correct agreement?
☐ What changes could be made to improve the letter?

Copyright © by Pearson Education, Inc.

Name _____ Date _____

What are the benefits of facing challenges?

READING 4: "The Great Fever"

VOCABULARY **Key Words** *Use with textbook page 127.*

Write each word in the box next to its definition.

| disease | experiment | fever | hypothesis | mosquitoes | virus |

Example: ___*disease*___ : an illness with specific symptoms affecting a person, animal, or plant

1. _____ : small flying biting insects that drink blood from people or animals, sometimes spreading diseases

2. _____ : a careful test you do to see how something will react in a certain situation, or to prove something is true

3. _____ : an idea that is suggested as an explanation for something, but is not yet proven to be true

4. _____ : a very small living thing that causes infectious illnesses

5. _____ : an illness in which you have a very high temperature

Use the words in the box at the top of the page to complete the sentences.

6. The scientists carried out an _____ in the chemistry lab.

7. In the garden, Lucy wears netting over her head to protect herself from

_____ .

8. Many diseases are caused by a single _____ .

9. The doctor was very worried about the child's high _____ .

10. People with a contagious _____ should stay at home.

Copyright © by Pearson Education, Inc.

Read the paragraph below. Pay attention to the underlined academic words.

Some psychologists believe that a person can <u>transmit</u> his or her mood to others. To test this <u>theory</u>, psychologists developed an experiment. The <u>objective</u> of the experiment was to see if people could transmit moods to a group. Two <u>volunteers</u> walked into a room full of people. The volunteers entered smiling and laughing. Soon, the others in the room were smiling and laughing, too!

Write the letter of the correct definition next to each word.

Example: ___*b*___ volunteers

_____ **1.** transmit

_____ **2.** theory

_____ **3.** objective

a. something that you are working hard to achieve

b. people who offer to do something without expecting to be paid

c. an idea that explains how something works or why something happens

d. send or pass something from one person to another

Use the academic words from the exercise above to complete the sentences.

4. The employees worked hard to reach their monthly _____.

5. All three _____ at the animal shelter were surprised when the manager offered to pay them.

6. The science experiment proved her _____.

7. The letter will _____ a message in code.

Complete the sentences with your own ideas.

Example: I believe the existence of ___*the Loch Ness Monster*___ is just a theory.

8. My main objective for the week is to _____.

9. I would like to volunteer in a _____.

10. I transmit notes to my friends by _____.

Copyright © by Pearson Education, Inc.

WORD STUDY Irregular Plurals *Use with textbook page 129.*

REMEMBER To make most nouns plural, add *-s* or *-es* to the end of the noun. However, some nouns are irregular and do not follow this pattern. For many singular nouns that end in consonant + *y*, change the *y* to *i* and add *-es*, as in *city—cities*. For singular nouns that end in *-is*, change the *-is* to *-es*, as in *neurosis—neuroses*.

Write the plural form of each noun.

Nouns that end in *consonant* + *y*		Nouns that end in *-is*	
Singular	**Plural**	**Singular**	**Plural**
Example: fly	*flies*	synthesis	*syntheses*
1. mystery		**6.** neurosis	
2. tragedy		**7.** axis	
3. memory		**8.** ellipsis	
4. opportunity		**9.** antithesis	
5. butterfly		**10.** oasis	

Write the plural form of each noun below.

Example: pony _____*ponies*_____

11. apology _____

12. parenthesis _____

13. synopsis _____

14. lady _____

15. puppy _____

Copyright © by Pearson Education, Inc.

Use with textbook page 129.

REMEMBER Recognizing cause and effect can help you better understand a text. Look for words and phrases such as *because, since, so that, therefore,* and *as a result of.*

Read the paragraph and answer the questions that follow.

Some students have something called test-taking anxiety. The thought of taking a test can keep them from studying well. This anxiety makes it difficult to concentrate when taking the test. Because of this nervousness, students will do poorly, even though they studied. Psychologists call it test anxiety and offer students tips on dealing with their feelings, so that they can perform better during tests.

1. **What is the cause in the paragraph?**

   _____

2. **What is the effect in the paragraph?**

   _____

Read the paragraph and answer the questions that follow.

Javan was excited about going camping. He became disappointed when the bus had to stop at the bridge. The river was high and flooded the bridge, so they couldn't get across to the campgrounds. As a result, the group got off the bus and crossed the river on foot in a place where the water was low. They hiked the rest of the way to the campsite.

3. What is the cause in the paragraph?

   _____

4. What is the effect in the paragraph?

   _____

5. How might the skill of identifying cause and effect help you when reading the text?

   _____

   _____

Copyright © by Pearson Education, Inc.

Name _____ Date _____

COMPREHENSION *Use with textbook page 134.*

Choose the best answer for each item. Circle the letter of the correct answer.

1. Yellow fever was feared because many people died from it and because _____.

   a. it led to more
   serious diseases

   b. it caused great
   suffering

   c. it caused people's skin
   to turn blue

2. Yellow fever got its name _____.

   a. because victims' skin
   and eyes turned
   yellow

   b. because victims
   liked yellow

   c. because yellow pills
   seemed to help cure
   the disease

3. Finlay believed that yellow fever is transmitted by _____.

   a. mosquitoes

   b. warm, damp air

   c. polluted water

4. Finlay created a map that showed that mosquito habitats and yellow fever epidemics

   were _____.

   a. in different seasons

   b. in the same places

   c. in very different places

5. In the 1930s, a vaccine was created to _____.

   a. kill mosquito eggs

   b. prevent jaundice

   c. prevent yellow fever

EXTENSION *Use with textbook page 135.*

Research five diseases. For each, note when it was discovered and tell when a cure was found or a vaccine was developed. If no cure or vaccine exists, note that as well.

Disease	Disease Discovered	Cure Found or Vaccine Developed
influenza	400 B.C.E.	1944

Copyright © by Pearson Education, Inc.

Passive Voice: Simple Past; Regular and Irregular Past Participles

Use with textbook page 136.

> **REMEMBER** Use the passive voice when the focus is on the receiver, not the performer, of an action.
> A *by*-phrase identifies the performer. **Example:** The election was won by the best candidate.
> Form the passive voice with the verb *be* + the past participle. Regular past participles are formed by adding *-d* or *-ed* to the base form of the verb. Irregular past participles must be memorized.
> **Example:** The cookies were eaten at the end of the club meeting.

Complete each sentence with the passive form of the verb in parentheses.

Example: (impress) The scientists ___were impressed___ by Finlay's theory.

1. (know) Yellow fever _____ as yellow jack.

2. (kill) Troops _____ by the deadly virus.

3. (study) Mosquitoes _____ by Dr. Carlos Finlay.

4. (train) Dr. Walter Reed _____ in the study of bacteria.

5. (find) No cure for yellow fever _____.

Rewrite each sentence using the passive voice.

Example: Ships carried the immature mosquitoes from Africa to America.
___The immature mosquitoes were carried by ships from Africa to America.___

6. Doctors and scientists read accounts of yellow fever.

_____

7. Yellow fever claimed millions of lives.

_____

8. Yellow fever struck the Mississippi Valley.

_____

9. The researchers proved the doctor's theory.

_____

10. Vaccines controlled yellow fever.

_____

Copyright © by Pearson Education, Inc.

GRAMMAR Passive Voice: Review *Use with textbook page 137.*

REMEMBER The passive voice can be used in any tense. Form the passive with a form of *be* +
the past participle. The *be* verb in a passive sentence reflects the tense in the active sentence. For
example, in the present perfect (*have* or *has* + past participle), the form of *be* in the passive is *has* or
have + the past participle of *be* (*been*).
If there is an object pronoun in an active sentence (*her*), it will change to a subject pronoun in passive
(*she*). The word order of the rest of the sentence in passive voice does not change. For example,
prepositional phrases that come at the beginning or end of an active voice sentence remain there in
passive voice.
Example: (active) Someone has pulled the car *out of the ditch*.
(passive) The car has been pulled *out of the ditch*.

**Write the tense of each sentence. Then rewrite each sentence using the passive
voice. Use the *by*-phrase only when necessary.**

Example: The young horse has eaten all the oats. _____ *present perfect* _____

     All the oats have been eaten by the young horse. _____

1. Someone has designed a new hybrid car. _____

_____

2. The gorilla crushed the tin can. _____

_____

3. Mr. Smith will give a test to our class. _____

_____

4. A person is giving a lecture on the planets at the community center.

    _____

_____

5. A new teacher is going to teach biology. _____

_____

6. Someone approached me from behind. _____

_____

Copyright © by Pearson Education, Inc.

Complete a three-column chart for a personal narrative about a memorable experience you had with a friend or classmate.

Who was there	What happened	What was said

Use the Peer Review Checklist below to obtain feedback from your partner. This feedback will help you edit your final draft.

PEER REVIEW CHECKLIST

☐ Does the paragraph describe a memorable event?
☐ Does the paragraph establish a time and place for the setting?
☐ Does the writer include dialogue to make the characters seem real?
☐ Did the story sustain my interest?
☐ Is passive voice used correctly?
☐ Are regular and irregular past participles used correctly?
☐ What changes could be made to improve the paragraph?

Copyright © by Pearson Education, Inc.

WRITING WORKSHOP   *Use with textbook pages 144–147.*

Organize your ideas in the graphic organizer below.

Characters	Setting	Problem	Solution

Use the Peer Review Checklist below to obtain feedback from your partner. This feedback will help you edit your final draft.

PEER REVIEW CHECKLIST

☐ Did the story sustain my interest?

☐ Is the story line engaging?

☐ Is the action well paced?

☐ Is the setting specific and believable?

☐ Are the characters interesting? Are they well developed?

☐ What changes could be made to improve the story?

Copyright © by Pearson Education, Inc.

Underline the vocabulary items you know and can use well. Review and practice any you haven't underlined. Underline them when you know them well.

Literary Words	Key Words	Academic Words	
characters	fugitive	accompanied	available
point of view	heritage	aid	injured
author's influences	network	challenge	structure
external conflict	runaway	code	survive
	shelter	approach	discriminate
	Underground Railroad	communicate	generation
	ancestry	resources	objective
	aviation	response	transmit
	career		volunteer
	curiosity		
	expensive		
	inferior		

Put a check by the skills you can perform well. Review and practice any you haven't checked off. Check them off when you can perform them well.

Skills	I can . . .
Word Study	☐ spell words using *ch* and *tch*. ☐ recognize and use prefixes *im-*, *over-*, *un-*, *after-*. ☐ recognize and use closed compound nouns. ☐ recognize and use consonant clusters.
Reading Strategies	☐ skim. ☐ identify problems and solutions. ☐ predict. ☐ recognize cause and effect.
Grammar	☐ use prepositions and present and past progressive. ☐ use gerunds as subjects, subject complements, and objects. ☐ use simple and compound sentences. ☐ use the passive voice.
Writing	☐ write a story with a starter. ☐ rewrite a familiar story. ☐ write a personal letter. ☐ write a personal narrative. ☐ write a fictional narrative.

Copyright © by Pearson Education, Inc.

Copyright © by Pearson Education, Inc.

TEST 1

DIRECTIONS
Look at the illustrations and answer the questions.

1 Where is the sign found?

   A   In a car
   B   In a store
   C   By the road
   D   By the door

2 A square is a quadrilateral. It is a rhombus because it has four congruent _____. It is a rectangle because it has four 90° angles. All squares are rectangles and rhombi, but all rhombi and rectangles are not squares.

   F   geometry
   G   similar
   H   sides
   J   shapes

DIRECTIONS
Read this selection. Then answer the questions that follow it.

Rosa Parks

1   One evening in December 1955, an African-American woman named Rosa Parks left work and boarded a bus in Montgomery, Alabama. She walked toward the back of the bus and sat down in the front row of the section of the bus where African Americans were forced to sit. The bus became crowded and the bus driver told Rosa Parks to give her seat to a white passenger. But Rosa Parks refused and was arrested by the police.

2   Rosa Parks was well-known in the Civil Rights Movement. The following night, Dr. Martin Luther King, Jr. met with other leaders who were fighting for equal rights for African Americans. They decided to protest Rosa Parks' arrest by leading a <u>boycott</u> of public buses in Montgomery. For over a year, most African Americans refused to ride the city's buses.

3   The Montgomery Bus Boycott led to other protests against segregation all over the South. In 1956 the judges of the U.S. Supreme Court ruled that African Americans could no longer be separated from white Americans on public buses. This helped end segregation.

---

1 What is paragraph 1 mainly about?

  A Why African Americans had to sit at the back of the bus

  B Why Rosa Parks was arrested

  C Why African Americans boycotted buses

  D Why Rosa Parks was well known

2 The selection is best described as —

  F informative

  G humorous

  H persuasive

  J expressive

3 What does the word *boycott* most likely mean?

  A To refuse to use a product or service

  B To fight for equal rights

  C To make a change

  D To force someone to do something

4 According to the selection, the arrest of Rosa Parks —

  F caught the attention of the Supreme Court

  G started protests that helped end segregation

  H happened when she was going to work

  J began the fight for equal rights

Copyright © by Pearson Education, Inc.

TEST 3

DIRECTIONS
Read this selection. Then answer the questions that follow it.

Avalanche Survivor

1   One winter day, 17-year-old J.D. Smith and four of his close friends went snowboarding on a remote mountainside outside of Denver, Colorado. They knew it was a risky area but couldn't resist the idea of snowboarding down the untouched, powdery snow.

2   Suddenly the group looked up to see an avalanche starting on the ridge above them. They tried to run but had not taken five steps before the snow was on top of them.

3   "I've never seen anything like it. It looked like pure white coming at us," Smith said later. "It sounded like an earthquake. Just by instinct, I knew that I had to get my hands up to my face, to make an air pocket. Then I just had to ride that snow all the way down and hope for the best."

4   The avalanche carried the boys about a quarter mile down the mountain. Smith was buried under three and a half feet of snow, but it was powdery, so he was able to dig himself out. He started searching for his friends, breaking off a tree branch to probe the snow. He didn't see the next avalanche coming. "It happened really fast," he recalled, "and it was over before I even knew it."

5   The second avalanche carried Smith all the way down to the bottom of the mountain. He was buried just 10 inches below the surface, but the snow was wet and packed, and he couldn't dig himself out. Eventually, he was able to get his head out of the hard snow and call for help. Smith had been trapped for more than an hour when someone nearby heard his calls and helped dig him out. Only one of Smith's friends also survived the powerful avalanches.

Copyright © by Pearson Education, Inc.

1 Look at the timeline.

Timeline of the Avalanches

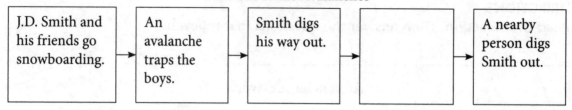

Which event BEST completes the timeline of events in the story?

A   Smith makes an air pocket with his hands.

B   An avalanche carried the boys down the mountain.

C   Smith probed the snow.

D   A second avalanche hits Smith.

2 Paragraph 4 is mainly about —

F   what happened after the first avalanche hit Smith

G   what the first avalanche looked like

H   what happened when the second avalanche hit the boys

J   what the second avalanche sounded like

3 Which of these is the BEST summary of the selection?

A   Smith and his friends go to a risky area to snowboard. Smith is buried. He digs out and looks for his friends. A nearby person helps him.

B   Smith and his friends go to a risky area to snowboard. An avalanche hits the boys. Another avalanche hits Smith. Smith is buried. He digs out and looks for his friends. A nearby person helps him.

(continued)

C   Smith and his friends go to a risky area to snowboard. An avalanche hits the boys. Smith is buried. He digs out and looks for his friends. A second avalanche hits Smith and buries him. Smith digs out enough to call for help. A nearby person helps him.

D   An avalanche hits the boys. Smith is buried. He digs out and looks for his friends. A second avalanche hits Smith and buries him. Smith digs out enough to call for help. A nearby person helps him.

4 According to the article, why did the boys go snowboarding in a risky area?

F   They did not think an avalanche could happen.

G   They did not know the area was risky.

H   They could not resist snowboarding on new snow.

J   They thought they could go faster than an avalanche.

Test Preparation

Copyright © by Pearson Education, Inc.

Visual Literacy: Smithsonian American
Art Museum *Use with textbook pages 150–151.*

LEARNING TO LOOK

Look at *The Sick Child* by J. Bond Francisco on page 151 in your textbook. Study the hands of the boy and the woman sitting beside him. Write three details about the boy's hands and the clown that he holds. State facts, not opinions.

Boy's Hands

Example: *He holds the clown by the leg.* _____

1. _____

2. _____

3. _____

Write three details about the woman's hands and the knitting needles she's working with.

Woman's Hands

4. _____

5. _____

6. _____

INTERPRETATION

Look at *The Sick Child* again. What might the woman be thinking? Write your answers below.

Example: *If only his fever would break, he would get well quickly!* _____

_____

_____

_____

_____

_____

_____

Copyright © by Pearson Education, Inc.

KWLH

Look at *Embroidered Garment* by Alice Eugenia Ligon on page 150 in your textbook. Use the artwork to complete the KWLH chart below.

K	W	L	H
What do you **know** about this work of art?	What do you **want** to learn about how the artist made it?	What have you **learned** about the artist and her work?	**How** did you learn this?
		She is a woman.	

Copyright © by Pearson Education, Inc.

UNIT 3 — How are relationships with others important?

READING 1: From *Salsa Stories* "Aguinaldo"

VOCABULARY **Literary Words** *Use with textbook page 155.*

> **REMEMBER** **Irony** is the difference between what happens and what a reader expects to happen in a story. Ironic situations can cause surprise and amusement. **Foreshadowing** is an author's use of clues to hint at what might happen later in a story. It builds suspense and shapes the reader's expectations.

Read the description of each situation. Write *irony* if it is an example of irony. Write *foreshadowing* if it is an example of foreshadowing.

Irony or foreshadowing?	Situation
foreshadowing	It was an unusually icy day when they began their car trip. The roads were slippery.
1.	Jeffrey drove for four straight days – only to end up back where he started.
2.	The policeman watched the customer with interest. Then he picked up his radio and said, "Chief, could you check on something for me?"
3.	Our team did well that day. But there were a lot of games left, and things didn't go well for very long . . .

Read the passage. Underline the elements of foreshadowing in the story.

> Miles threw his shoes and shirt into the closet carelessly. He looked down at his desk. There was an unopened letter sitting there, but he tried not to look at it. He opened the window, then shut it again for no reason. The clock seemed to tick more loudly than before. He looked at the picture of his family hanging on the wall. *What if it's bad news?* he thought. He went downstairs for a glass of water, but once he got to the kitchen he forgot to pour it. He thought of his brother, and how much time had passed since his previous letter. Why would he write now? A moment passed. "OK then," Miles said. He marched upstairs, ready for anything. Even bad news.

4. What do you think happens next? _____

Copyright © by Pearson Education, Inc.

Read the paragraph below. Pay attention to the underlined academic words.

There is a non-profit organization in our town that <u>distributes</u> free lunches to the elderly. Volunteers bring the lunches to elderly <u>residents</u>' homes every day at noon. No elderly person who requests a free lunch is ever <u>rejected</u>. Both volunteers and the elderly find delivering and receiving free lunches a very <u>positive</u> experience.

Write the letter of the correct definition next to each word.

Example: ___*b*___ rejected

_____ **1.** residents

_____ **2.** distributes

_____ **3.** positive

a. gives something to different people or places

b. decided not to do something

c. good or useful

d. people who live in a place

Use the academic words from the exercise above to complete the sentences.

4. Even though the situation was unpleasant, she tried to keep a

_____ attitude.

5. All the _____ of the apartment building helped to keep the grounds clean.

6. He _____ the man's offer of payment when he saw how poor the man was.

7. Every Sunday she _____ flyers to her neighbors to advertise her crafts store.

Complete the sentences with your own ideas.

Example: I had a very positive experience while ___*volunteering at the soup kitchen*___.

8. If I ask a friend to go out for the evening and am rejected, I usually feel

_____.

9. I like the residents of my neighborhood because _____.

10. Before each class, my teacher distributes _____.

Copyright © by Pearson Education, Inc.

WORD STUDY **Spelling *s-* Blends** *Use with textbook page 157.*

REMEMBER A consonant blend is two or three consonants that are placed together in a word. You can hear the sound of each consonant in a consonant blend.

Look at the words in the word box. Underline the consonant blend that begins each word. Then write each word in the correct category in the chart.

sport	stall	strength	swing	spell	stand	strange	swell	spend	store

sw-	sp-	st-	str-
swing			

Complete each sentence by adding the correct *s-* blend in the space provided.

1. I want to _____**end** more time at home.

2. My favorite _____**ort** is soccer.

3. I have to stay in bed so that I can recover my _____**ength**.

4. I do not know how to _____**ell** that word.

5. It was a very _____**ange** movie.

6. I have a _____**omachache**.

7. My parents always make me feel _____**ecial**.

8. I am going to the _____**ore** to buy milk.

Copyright © by Pearson Education, Inc.

Use with textbook page 157.

REMEMBER Analyzing the cultural context of a story helps you visualize and understand what's happening. Notice the author's descriptions and think about the characters' language, country, ideas, and beliefs. Also, think of what you know from your own experiences.

Read each paragraph and answer the questions that follow.

I didn't know what to expect when David invited me to his Chanukah party. He explained that Chanukah was the Jewish festival of lights. We played a game with a four-sided top called a dreidel to win the most Chanukah gelt—foil-wrapped chocolate candy. Later, he and his family lit a special candleholder called a menorah. We had delicious potato pancakes called latkes and later we had special Chanukah doughnuts called sufganiot. Yum!

1. What culture does the narrator experience?

_____

2. What does the narrator learn about the culture of the family he or she visits?

_____

_____

3. How does the family in this passage feel about their culture?

_____

_____

4. Did you learn anything new about Chanukah from this passage?

_____

_____

5. How do you think the strategy of recognizing a story's cultural context can help you read with better comprehension?

_____

_____

Copyright © by Pearson Education, Inc.

COMPREHENSION   *Use with textbook page 166.*

Choose the best answer for each item. Circle the letter of the correct answer.

1. Marilia doesn't want to go on the trip to the nursing home because _____.

   a. she is sick   **b.** her grandmother   **c.** nursing homes are
                                 died in one   boring

2. An *aguinaldo* is a _____.

   a. nursing home   **b.** coconut sweet   **c.** surprise Christmas gift
       patient

3. The morning of the trip, Marilia _____.

   a. is excited   **b.** refuses to leave home   **c.** pretends to be sick

4. During her time with Elenita, Marilia feels _____.

   a. happy   **b.** angry   **c.** bored

5. The main irony of the story is that Marilia _____.

   a. spoke to an   **b.** tried to escape her   **c.** received an *aguinaldo*
       elderly woman   obligations but couldn't   of her own

RESPONSE to LITERATURE   *Use with textbook page 167.*

By the end of the story, Marilia has made a new friend. If the story continues, and Marilia visits the nursing home again, what do you think will happen?

_____

_____

_____

_____

_____

Copyright © by Pearson Education, Inc.

REMEMBER Imperatives are often used to give a command or instructions. Form an imperative with the simple present, omitting the subject *you*. To make an imperative negative, add *do not* or *don't* before the verb.
Examples: *Turn on* the oven. *Don't touch* it! It's hot!
Use *please* before an imperative to make a request or offer. Use *let's* before an imperative to include yourself in a suggestion.
Examples: Please come *with me. Let's go* together.

Underline all the imperatives and circle all the negative imperatives in the recipe.

Preheat oven to 360 degrees. Mix butter, eggs, and sugar until foamy. Slowly add flour to butter-egg-sugar mixture. In a separate bowl, stir cocoa into a third of the dough. Don't use all the cocoa. Now it is time to pour the dough into the baking pan, alternating layers of light and dark dough. Use a fork to create a pattern. Place the baking pan into the preheated oven.

Rewrite each sentence using an imperative.

Example: You need to use two pieces of bread.

Use two pieces of bread.

1. First you need to use a knife to put peanut butter on both slices.

2. Then you should spread the jelly evenly on both slices of bread.

3. After that, you need to put one slice of bread on top of the other.

4. Next it is time to cut the sandwich in half diagonally.

5. Now you can enjoy your sandwich.

Copyright © by Pearson Education, Inc.

Embedded Questions *Use with textbook page 169.*

> **REMEMBER** An embedded question is a type of noun clause and can be the subject or object of a sentence. Embedded information questions begin with a question word, such as *what* or *when*. Embedded *yes / no* questions begin with *if* or *whether*. Use normal word order (subject + verb) for embedded questions. The noun clause is often preceded by phrases such as *I don't know . . .*, *I wonder . . .*, and *Could you tell me . . . ?*

Complete each sentence with an embedded question, using the question in parentheses.

Example: ___*How he finished early*___ I'll never know. (How did he finish early?)

1. I wonder _____. (What time does the bus come?)

2. Do you know _____? (Where did Sarah go last night?)

3. I can't remember _____. (What is your address?)

4. _____ is on everybody's mind. (Who will come to the party?)

Correct the errors in the embedded questions in the following sentences.

Example: Do you know what time is it? ___*Do you know what time it is?*___

5. I don't know where did she go. _____

6. I wonder what does he do. _____

7. Can you tell me who is she? _____

8. I'm not sure when does class begin. _____

Copyright © by Pearson Education, Inc.

Complete your own sequence chart containing instructions for something you know how to do well.

First

↓

Then

↓

Next

↓

Finally

Use the Peer Review Checklist below to obtain feedback from your partner. This feedback will help you edit your final draft.

PEER REVIEW CHECKLIST

☐ Does the first sentence introduce the main idea?

☐ Are the instructions clear and easy to follow?

☐ Are the instructions given in the correct order?

☐ Does the writer use transition words to make the sequence clear?

☐ Are imperatives and embedded questions used correctly?

☐ What changes could be made to improve the paragraph?

Copyright © by Pearson Education, Inc.

Name _____ Date _____

VOCABULARY **Key Words** *Use with textbook page 173.*

Write each word in the box next to its definition.

barriers	confront	cultivate	~~enemies~~	political	violence

Example: ___*enemies*___: people who hate you or want to harm you

1. _____: relating to the government of a country

2. _____: try to develop a friendship with someone who can help you

3. _____: things that prevent people from doing something

4. _____: address someone or something

5. _____: behavior that is intended to hurt other people physically

Use the words in the box at the top of the page to complete the sentences.

6. The government wants to keep any of its _____ from getting
   too strong.

7. It's good to _____ friendships with people who share your interests.

8. Their _____ differences led to an argument about government.

9. He had to _____ the difficult situation.

10. _____ is not the way to solve a problem, because we should try to
    solve things peacefully.

Copyright © by Pearson Education, Inc.

Read the paragraph below. Pay attention to the underlined academic words.

> When I first met Sanaya, I <u>assumed</u> we could never be friends. She wore very strange clothes and her hair was dyed pink. But I remembered what my mother always said: "Don't judge a book by its cover." One shouldn't just <u>focus</u> on appearance. We are all <u>individuals</u> and each person has value. So I decided that if I just tried talking to Sanaya, maybe I would like her. I was right! We discovered we had many <u>similarities</u>. Now she is my best friend.

Write the academic words from the paragraph above next to their correct definitions.

Example: _____*focus*_____: pay special attention to a particular person or thing instead of others

1. _____: the qualities of being similar, or the same

2. _____: thought that something was true without having proof

3. _____: people; not a whole group

Use the academic words from the paragraph above to complete the sentences.

4. The students preferred to receive their diplomas one at a time, as

   _____.

5. The student _____ he had done well on the test, but he was wrong.

6. The girls learned that their _____ were as important as their differences.

7. This week in history class we will _____ on the War of the Roses.

Complete the sentences with your own ideas.

Example: Two similarities between my friend and me are
   our tempers and our interest in history.

8. After school I like to focus on _____.

9. For a long time, I assumed that _____.

10. I think that it's important for people to be treated as individuals because

    _____.

Copyright © by Pearson Education, Inc.

WORD STUDY Suffixes *-er, -or* Use with textbook page 175.

REMEMBER A suffix is a letter or group of letters placed at the end of a base word. Adding a suffix changes the meaning of the base word. Adding the suffix *-er* or *-or* to a base word adds the meaning "one who." **Example:** *Traveler* means "one who travels."

Look at the base words and suffixes in the chart. Add the suffix *-er* or *-or* to create a new word. Then write the definition of the word using the verbs in the box.

| teach | sing | play | facilitate | create | visit | act | read | ~~write~~ | own |

Base Word	+ Suffix	= New Word	Definition
write	-er	*writer*	*one who writes*
1. instruct	-or		
2. perform	-er		
3. inspect	-or		
4. believe	-er		
5. create	-or		
6. review	-er		
7. edit	-or		
8. direct	-or		

Complete each sentence by adding *-er* or *-or* in the space provided. Use a dictionary if needed.

9. The act _____ was great in his role as a spy.

10. Diego is the best play _____ on our soccer team.

11. The artist was a brilliant sculpt _____.

12. My mother is the own _____ of a business.

13. We have a visit _____ at our school today.

14. Mr. Jones is my favorite teach _____.

15. I'd like to be a photograph _____.

Copyright © by Pearson Education, Inc.

Use with textbook page 175.

> **REMEMBER** When you compare, you see how things are similar. When you contrast, you see how things are different. Comparing and contrasting can help you understand what you read.

Read each paragraph. Then answer the questions that follow.

Dara and Dora are identical twins. They look the same with dark hair and big brown eyes. Their friends call them opposites, however. Dara is smart but grumpy. Dora is pleasant but lazy.

1. How are Dara and Dora alike?

_____

_____

2. How are Dara and Dora different?

_____

_____

The United Kingdom and the United States have a lot in common. English is the first language in both countries. Both countries have been the most powerful nations in the world. However, the United Kingdom is small and the United States is large. In the U.K., people love soccer, rugby and cricket; in the U.S. they favor football, basketball, and baseball—although soccer is becoming more popular than ever.

3. How are the United States and the United Kingdom alike?

_____

_____

4. What are some differences between the United Kingdom and the United States?

_____

_____

5. How can comparing and contrasting make you a better reader?

_____

_____

Copyright © by Pearson Education, Inc.

COMPREHENSION   *Use with textbook page 180.*

Choose the best answer for each item. Circle the letter of the correct answer.

1. The purpose of Seeds of Peace is to _____.

   a. teach people how to argue about politics and religion
   b. help bring understanding to the Middle East
   c. perform research on kids

2. Seeds of Peace combines regular camp activities with _____.

   a. two-hour "coexistence sessions"
   b. international competitions
   c. history lessons about Palestine and Israel

3. In the bunk, the girls argue about _____.

   a. tourism in Jerusalem
   b. which religion is better and more ancient
   c. control of the city of Jerusalem

4. The article asks you to compare and contrast the views of _____.

   a. Middle Eastern children
   b. students and counselors
   c. children and politicians

5. Both Eitan and Marisa imply that they are happy that _____.

   a. they learned about rowing in canoes
   b. they got time off from school
   c. they made new friends

EXTENSION   *Use with textbook page 181.*

Look up five areas of the world where conflict and war are ongoing. Who is involved in each conflict? How long has it gone on? Write the results of your research in the chart.

Location	Who is involved?	How long?
Iraq	Sunnis, Shiites, Kurds, United States	since 2003

Copyright © by Pearson Education, Inc.

REMEMBER A complex sentence consists of a main clause and at least one subordinate clause joined with a subordinating conjunction. A main clause has a subject and a verb and expresses a complete thought. A subordinate clause has a subject and a verb, but does NOT express a complete thought. When a complex sentence begins with a subordinate clause, a comma follows the clause.

Underline the subordinate clause(s) and circle the main clause in each sentence.

Example: (When Noor joined the camp,) he didn't know that he would meet Shirlee.

1. At the camp, Arabs and Israelis meet for the first time and they learn to get along.

2. Sometimes the campers fight with each other because they disagree.

3. Although the Arab and Israeli students disagree on many topics, before Seeds of Peace, they disagreed even more.

4. Until Arabs and Israelis can agree on Jerusalem, there will always be problems.

5. Before Seeds of Peace, many children would not have been friends.

Join the clauses with the subordinating conjunction in parentheses.

6. (because) The camp was amazing. I learned a lot about the world.

   _____

7. (before) The situation got out of control. The counselors would help us talk about the issues.

   _____

8. (although) Many of our discussions were heated. We never got angry at each other.

   _____

9. (because) I made new friends. There were so many interesting people.

   _____

10. (after) I told my friends about Seeds of Peace. They wanted to join.

   _____

Copyright © by Pearson Education, Inc.

Agreement in Complex Sentences *Use with textbook page 183.*

> **REMEMBER** The main and subordinate clauses in a complex sentence should be in the same tense. When a clause is in present tense and has a singular subject, be sure to use a singular verb. Also, pronouns must agree with their antecedents. In the example, both clauses are in the present tense. The singular subject, *Allie*, agrees with the verb *wants*; the singular subject *she* agrees with *needs*. The pronoun *she* agrees with its antecedent, *Allie*, and the pronoun *them* agrees with its antecedent, *Paul and David*.
>
> **Example:** If *Allie wants* to drive with *Paul and David*, *she needs* to call *them* right away.

Correct the errors in verb tense in the following sentences.

                      loves   *has*
Example: Every mother ~~love~~ her child because she ~~had~~ an instinct to.

1. When John slipped and fell, he were running down the stairs.

2. I doesn't know where I was going. Can you help me?

3. While we was eating dinner, the phone rings.

4. Until spring come, we isn't planting our garden.

Complete each sentence with the correct pronoun(s) that agrees with the underlined antecedent.

Example: Although <u>the cat</u> was fat, <u>it</u> was very active.

5. <u>The children</u> stayed in _____ rooms because _____ were being punished.

6. Although <u>John</u> forgot _____ lines during rehearsal,

    _____ remembered them during the performance.

7. <u>The boy</u> ate _____ snack after _____ finished his homework.

8. <u>Children</u> sometimes have toys that _____ carry with

    _____ until _____ start school.

Copyright © by Pearson Education, Inc.

Complete your own content web with ideas for a critique of a story, movie, video game, or place you have visited.

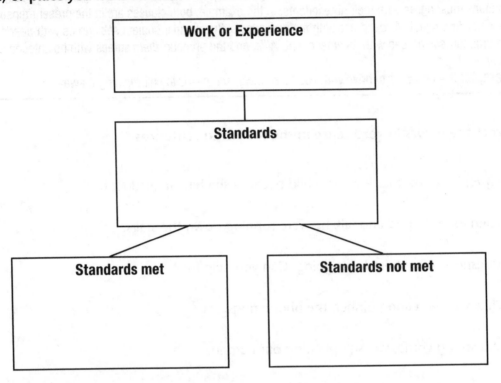

Use the Peer Review Checklist below to obtain feedback from your partner. This feedback will help you edit your final draft.

PEER REVIEW CHECKLIST

☐ Does the first sentence introduce the topic?

☐ Does the paragraph clearly identify the criteria for evaluation?

☐ Does the writer evaluate the event or experience according to the criteria?

☐ Is the writer's opinion clear?

☐ Are connecting words used to link ideas and create complex sentences?

☐ Do nouns and pronouns agree in complex sentences?

☐ What changes could be made to improve the paragraph?

Copyright © by Pearson Education, Inc.

UNIT 3

How are relationships with others important?

READING 3: From *Blue Willow*

VOCABULARY **Literary Words** *Use with textbook page 187.*

> **REMEMBER** **Oral tradition** is the practice of storytellers passing stories down from one generation to the next. These stories sometimes included a **legend**, or traditional story that moves away from factual events to describe more fictional events and characters. A **character motive** is a reason that explains a character's thoughts, feelings, action, and speech.

For each situation listed, give the motivation of the main character.

Motivation	Situation
fatigue	Luke put down the ax and wiped his brow. Almost done, he thought, and then I can finally go to sleep!
1.	"I don't want to see it," Deng said. He backed away from the display slowly, shaking. "It's too awful to even think about," he added.
2.	DeWayne looked greedily at the stack of $20 bills that would be given out as prizes. He grinned and rubbed his hands. "I'd like to enter the contest," he said.
3.	Corrina looked at the clock every few minutes. When the day was over, her parents would arrive. If she could have made time move faster by working harder, she would have.

Does one of the passages have the characteristics of a legend? Write *yes* or *no*.

4. _____ Thor raised his hammer and struck the earth to scare away the fiery dragon. Behind the dragon he could see treasure boxes spilling over with gold.

5. _____ The weather in Miami, Florida, is often humid and hot. Even in the winter, the temperatures can be in the high 70s and low 80s.

Copyright © by Pearson Education, Inc.

Read the paragraph below. Pay attention to the underlined academic words.

John's uncle is an <u>authoritative</u> figure among the Dagomba people of northern Ghana. He is a griot—someone who tells stories through music. John had always wanted to visit him. Last month, after getting the <u>consent</u> of his uncle, John's parents surprised him with a plane ticket to Ghana. His <u>reaction</u> was pure excitement. John spent two weeks in Ghana and his uncle taught him how to play a "talking drum." John's <u>encounter</u> with his uncle was one he will never forget.

Write the letter of the correct definition next to each word.

Example: ___c___ reaction

_____ 1. authoritative

_____ 2. encounter

_____ 3. consent

a. respected and trusted as being true, or making people respect or obey you

b. an occasion when you meet someone without planning to

c. the way you behave in response to someone or something

d. permission to do something

Use the academic words from the exercise above to complete the sentences.

4. The forest ranger had an unexpected _____ with a grizzly bear.

5. The students all had a positive _____ to the field-trip announcement.

6. Before the operation could begin, the patient had to give her _____.

7. This article contains several mistakes, so it is not an _____ source.

Complete the sentences with your own ideas.

Example: ___*The Senator*___ is an authoritative leader.

8. When I get bad news, my reaction can range from

_____ to _____.

9. I need parental consent before I can _____.

10. I once had a funny encounter with _____.

Copyright © by Pearson Education, Inc.

WORD STUDY **Synonyms** *Use with textbook page 189.*

REMEMBER Synonyms are words that have the same or nearly the same meaning.
Example: *loud* and *noisy*

For each word in column 1, find its synonym in column 2. Write the letter of the synonym next to each word.

1. pretty _____   **a.** costly

2. kind _____   **b.** cruel

3. mean _____   **c.** nice

4. large _____   **d.** attractive

5. expensive _____   **e.** big

For each of the words below, write a synonym. Use a thesaurus or dictionary if needed.

6. ask _____

7. inform _____

8. knowledge _____

9. shout _____

10. detest _____

11. beautiful _____

12. small _____

13. clever _____

14. unusual _____

15. cheap _____

Copyright © by Pearson Education, Inc.

Use with textbook page 189.

> **REMEMBER** When you identify with a character, you try to understand the actions and feelings of a character. This can help you enjoy and understand a story.

Read each paragraph. Then answer the questions that follow.

Martina saw that Grayson had left his social studies test right on the library table. Nobody else was around. If she wanted to, she could take a quick look at his answers. After all, Grayson was the most brilliant student in the class. Martina hadn't taken the test herself. But on the other hand, what would Grandma Rose think if she found out that her granddaughter was a cheater? *I need a good grade!* she thought. *What should I do?*

1. What choice is Martina facing in this passage?

   _____

2. What would you do if you were Martina, and why?

   _____

   _____

Zach loved creating music. He played guitar, drums, and piano, and recorded his songs on his computer. He knew they were getting better all the time. However he had a problem: when he opened his mouth to sing, he was always off-key. Then he learned about the band contest. The winner could get a scholarship to music school. It was everything he dreamed about. How could he show how good his music was when he couldn't sing?

3. What does the main character care about in this passage?

   _____

4. What problem does Zach face in this passage?

   _____

   _____

5. How can the strategy of identifying with a character help you become a better reader?

   _____

   _____

Copyright © by Pearson Education, Inc.

COMPREHENSION   *Use with textbook page 198.*

Choose the best answer for each item. Circle the letter of the correct answer.

1. Kung Shi Fair and Chang the Good _____.

   a. never meet   **b.** are sworn enemies   **c.** fall in love
       in the story

2. The merchant attempts to _____.

   a. keep Kung Shi Fair   **b.** scare the villagers   **c.** bring people together
       and Chang the   with stories about
       Good apart   a ferocious leopard

3. Kung Shi Fair and Chang believe that _____.

   a. they will kill   **b.** one day they   **c.** the merchant will bring
       the leopard   will marry   them gifts

4. The merchant insists that Kung Shi Fair wait for _____.

   a. two swallows   **b.** a rainbow   **c.** a bolt of lightning

5. If the merchant had not been so stubborn, then perhaps _____.

   a. his daughter would   **b.** he would have caught   **c.** Chang might never have
       have lived   the leopard   met Kung Shi Fair

RESPONSE TO LITERATURE   *Use with textbook page 199.*

Write a different ending to the story *Blue Willow*. Tell what might have happened if Kung Shi Fair's father had approved of the poor fisherman.

_____

_____

_____

_____

_____

Copyright © by Pearson Education, Inc.

GRAMMAR **Transitions to Show Contrast and Cause-and-Effect**

Use with textbook page 200.

REMEMBER The transitions and transitional phrases *however*, *on the other hand*, and *instead* contrast two ideas. *As a result*, *therefore*, *thus*, and *consequently* show cause-and-effect. Use a period when a transition or transitional phrase connects two sentences; use a semicolon when connecting two independent clauses. A comma follows a transition or transitional phrase when it begins a sentence or clause. Commas offset a transitional phrase midsentence, but a comma is not used with most one-word transitions midsentence. One exception is *consequently*, which is offset with commas.

Circle all the correct transitions to complete each sentence.

Example: Jerome volunteered for the Peace Corps. (However /(As a result)/(Therefore)), he went into relief work.

1. She didn't like the blue dress. (Thus / Instead / However), she liked the green one.

2. The principal awarded Roger honors. Roger, (as a result / on the other hand / consequently), went to the best university.

3. Marcia ate too much cake; (consequently / instead / thus), she had a stomachache.

4. I'm not fond of fish. (Instead / Therefore / On the other hand), I love shellfish.

Add punctuation (commas, semicolons, and periods) to correct the use of the transitions in the sentences below.

5. Becky studies a lot therefore she gets good grades.

6. Adam doesn't like to play video games instead he enjoys reading.

7. We practiced every day for weeks Consequently the concert was a success.

8. Chuck was hungry after running As a result he ate six eggs.

Copyright © by Pearson Education, Inc.

Transitions to Show Similarity and Add Information

Use with textbook page 201.

REMEMBER The transitions and transitional phrases *similarly*, *as well*, and *likewise* show similarity. *Also*, *besides*, *furthermore*, and *in addition* add new information; *in fact* and *indeed* add further information. Transitions and transitional phrases can begin a sentence or clause, or appear midsentence. Some transitions and phrases, such as *also*, *as well*, *besides*, and *in fact* can be used at the end of a sentence or clause. A comma follows transitions and transitional phrases when they begin sentences or clauses. Don't use a comma with most one-word transitions midsentence, except for *furthermore*.

Complete each sentence with a correct transition. More than one answer may be possible.

Example: The cake was delicious. _*Indeed*_, it was the best cake I'd ever eaten.

1. The store carries jams from Hungary; _____, it has chocolates from Belgium.

2. Peter has five dogs. _____, his brother has five cats.

3. The children went to the zoo. They went out for ice cream _____.

4. The lecture was really interesting; _____, it was the most interesting lecture I'd heard in a long time.

Complete the sentences with your own ideas.

Example: I enjoy _*mountain biking*_. Indeed, _*I go most weekends*_.

5. I enjoy _____. Indeed, _____.

6. My best friend _____; similarly, _____.

7. Sometimes I go _____. In fact, _____.

8. Our school has _____. It _____ besides.

Copyright © by Pearson Education, Inc.

Use with textbook pages 202–203.

Complete your own Venn diagram comparing and contrasting two people, places, or things you know well.

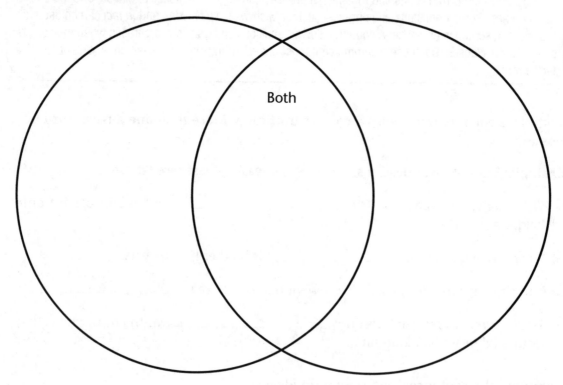

Both

Use the Peer Review Checklist below to obtain feedback from your partner. This feedback will help you edit your final draft.

PEER REVIEW CHECKLIST

☐ Does the first sentence explain what is being compared or contrasted?

☐ Does the paragraph describe similarities and differences?

☐ Does the paragraph include specific examples to support the main points?

☐ Are compare and contrast structures used correctly?

☐ Are transitions used to show cause and effect?

☐ What changes could be made to improve the paragraph?

Copyright © by Pearson Education, Inc.

Name _____ Date _____

How are relationships with others important?

READING 4: "The Ladybird and the Wildflowers"

VOCABULARY **Key Words** *Use with textbook page 205.*

Write each word in the box next to its definition.

carbon dioxide	conservation	native	nature	~~oxygen~~	symbiotic

Example: ____*oxygen*____: a gas that has no color, smell, or taste and that all plants and animals need in order to live

1. _____: growing, living, or produced in a particular area

2. _____: describing the relationship between two living things that exist closely together and depend on each other for advantages

3. _____: the protection of plants and types of animals

4. _____: the gas produced when people and animals breathe out

5. _____: the world and everything in it that people have not made, such as plants, animals, and the weather

Use the words in the box at the top of the page to complete the sentences.

6. Animals with a(n) _____ relationship live near each other.

7. Scientists are studying what happens when there is too much _____ in the air.

8. Parents should teach their children about _____ of plants and animals.

9. As you breathe, your lungs send _____ into your blood.

10. It is better to have plants that are _____ to an area because they are usually healthier.

Copyright © by Pearson Education, Inc.

Read the paragraph below. Pay attention to the underlined academic words.

Many species <u>interact</u> with other species. Some, though, form a special <u>partnership</u> called a *symbiotic relationship*. Each partner plays a <u>role</u> that is <u>beneficial</u> to the other. For example, when a bee gathers food from a flower, it gets the flower's pollen on it. Then, when it visits another flower of the same kind, it leaves some of the pollen behind. This allows the flower to make seeds.

Write the academic words from the paragraph above next to their correct definitions.

Example: _____*role*_____ : the position or job that something or someone has in a particular situation or activity

1. _____ : talk to other people and work together with them

2. _____ : a relationship in which two or more people, organizations, etc., work together to achieve something

3. _____ : good or useful

Use the academic words from the paragraph above to complete the sentences.

4. The two journalists formed a _____ to share information.

5. Donna's _____ at the store is to change the window display every week.

6. Her advice turned out to be very _____ .

7. If you work from home instead of at an office, you don't _____ with many people during the day.

Complete the sentences with your own ideas.

Example: Immigrants are beneficial to a neighborhood because of
___*the culture they bring*___ .

8. The first person I interact with in the morning is _____ .

9. One important role I have in my family is _____ .

10. I have a partnership with _____ .

Copyright © by Pearson Education, Inc.

WORD STUDY Sound-Letter Relationships

Use with textbook page 207.

> **REMEMBER** In English, the letters *th* are said together to make one sound. There are two ways to say the sound *th*. The first way is the soft sound, as in the word *with*. The other *th* sound is hard, as in the word *the*.

Look at the chart below.

Soft Sound *with*	Hard Sound *the*
thrive	either
thing	these

Choose <u>soft sound</u> or <u>hard sound</u> for each word.

1. together

    a. soft sound   **b.** hard sound

2. truth

    a. soft sound   **b.** hard sound

3. then

    a. soft sound   **b.** hard sound

4. author

    a. soft sound   **b.** hard sound

5. think

    a. soft sound   **b.** hard sound

6. breathe

    a. soft sound   **b.** hard sound

Write sentences using four of the words above.

7. _____

8. _____

9. _____

10. _____

Copyright © by Pearson Education, Inc.

> **REMEMBER** When you classify, you arrange words, ideas, objects, texts, or people into groups with common characteristics.

Read the paragraph. Then answer the questions that follow.

My mom laughs when she sees cars pulling up near the house that is three doors down from us. She knows that the drivers are amazed by the Seavers' house. The Seavers love the holidays—all holidays. Whether it's Martin Luther King, Jr. Day, Valentine's Day, Washington's Birthday, Easter, or July 4, the Seavers have their house covered with decorations. On President's Day, they had 100 little flags sticking up in their lawn. On Valentine's Day, every window had cut-out hearts. For Halloween, they covered their yard with fake spiderwebs. Dad frowns disapprovingly, "That looks like too much work." But I agree with my mom. I think the Seavers make all the holidays more fun.

1. List words in this passage that have to do with emotions.

   _____

   _____

2. List words in this passage that have to do with decorations.

   _____

   _____

3. List words in this passage that are holidays.

   _____

   _____

4. List how each member of the writer's family feels about the Seavers.

   _____

   _____

5. How do you think classifying can make you a better reader?

   _____

   _____

Name _____ Date _____

Choose the best answer for each item. Circle the letter of the correct answer.

1. Lady Bird Johnson loved trees and flowers _____.

   a. when she became   **b.** after studying them   **c.** since childhood
   First Lady   in college

2. New plants brought into an area _____ native plants.

   a. hurt   **b.** help   **c.** have no effect on

3. After Lady Bird was not First Lady, she _____ the environment.

   a. asked other First   **b.** stopped helping   **c.** still helped
   Ladies to help

4. It is _____ for animals to eat native plants.

   a. healthy   **b.** unhealthy   **c.** unusual

5. Lady Bird believed that people _____ help the environment.

   a. can't   **b.** want to   **c.** don't know how to

EXTENSION   *Use with textbook page 213.*

What is another good idea for a First Lady's project? Do you know if a First Lady had this project? If so, describe what she did. If not, what do you think a First Lady should do for this project?

_____

_____

_____

_____

_____

Copyright © by Pearson Education, Inc.

GRAMMAR **More about Antecedent / Pronoun Agreement**

Use with textbook page 214.

REMEMBER All pronouns must agree in number and gender with their antecedents. For example, if the antecedent is a singular, feminine noun, the pronouns must also be singular and feminine.
Example: *Deirdre* locked *herself* out of *her* car.
A generic noun refers to a whole group; it does not have a gender since it does not refer to anything in particular. When a singular generic noun refers to a person, use any singular pronoun that names a person. When a singular generic noun refers to a thing, use a neutral pronoun. When a generic noun is plural, use a plural pronoun.
Examples: When *a child* cries, *she* usually wants *her* mother.
Something fell, but I don't know what *it* was.
People always like to hear *themselves* talk.

Circle all the correct pronouns to complete each sentence.

Example: A student should always do (his)/ (her)/ its) homework.

1. Somebody left (his / its / her) cell phone in the cafeteria.

2. The cat ran under the fence, and (it / he / they) ran up a tree.

3. I get worried when the neighbors let (its / his / their) dog out.

4. Everyone needs to pick up (his / her / my) own trash.

5. Paul and I are riding (his / our / her) bikes through the park.

6. Even though the party was fun, (he / they / it) was crowded.

7. When a person has a car accident, (I / he / she) should pull off the road.

8. Katie and Adam are concerned about (his / her / their) grades.

Copyright © by Pearson Education, Inc.

Parallel Structure *Use with textbook page 215.*

> **REMEMBER** Using parallel structure means that words, phrases, or clauses connected with conjunctions have a similar pattern.
> **Examples:** *The birds*, *the bees*, and *the flowers* help each other. [all plural verbs]
> Birds start *to build their nests in spring*, but they don't begin *to mate until later*. [both infinitive phrases]
> When winter *comes*, the flowers *die*. [both simple present verbs]
> The animals *were given* shelter after they *were fed*. [both clauses in passive voice]

Choose the best word or phrase to complete each sentence.

Example: We were hungry, cold, and (sleepy / felt like sleeping).

1. I have met his brother, but I (didn't meet / haven't met) his sister.

2. They love skiing and (to snowboard / snowboarding).

3. Plants need light, (to have enough water / enough water), and an appropriate climate.

4. Italy has warm beaches, great restaurants, and (Roman architecture / architecture from the Romans).

Combine the pairs of sentences with the conjunction in parentheses, making one sentence that has parallel structure.

Example: Ben is generous. Ben is honest. Ben is kind. (and)

   Ben is generous, honest, and kind. _____

5. Mae opened the door. Mae greeted her guests. (after)

   _____ .

6. We had a quiz on Friday. We had a test on Friday. (before)

   _____ .

7. She quit her job. She moved to New York. She became an actor. (and)

   _____ .

Copyright © by Pearson Education, Inc.

Use with textbook pages 216–217.

Complete your own three-column chart classifying something into three categories.

Use the Peer Review Checklist below to obtain feedback from your partner. This feedback will help you edit your final draft.

PEER REVIEW CHECKLIST

☐ Does the first sentence introduce the topic?

☐ Does the paragraph include three different categories within the topic?

☐ Does the paragraph explain why each category is different from the others?

☐ Is there an example for each category?

☐ Was the information interesting?

☐ Do pronouns agree with their antecedents?

☐ What changes could be made to improve the paragraph?

Copyright © by Pearson Education, Inc.

WRITING WORKSHOP *Use with textbook pages 222–225.*

Organize your ideas in the graphic organizer below.

Use the Peer Review Checklist below to obtain feedback from your partner. This feedback will help you edit your final draft.

PEER REVIEW CHECKLIST

- ☐ Was the essay clearly organized?
- ☐ Was the information interesting?
- ☐ Did I understand the topic better after reading it?
- ☐ Did the first paragraph introduce the topic?
- ☐ Did the concluding paragraph sum up the main points?
- ☐ What changes could be made to improve the essay?

Copyright © by Pearson Education, Inc.

Underline the vocabulary items you know and can use well. Review and practice any you haven't underlined. Underline them when you know them well.

Literary Words	Key Words	Academic Words	
foreshadowing	barriers	distributes	authoritative
irony	confront	positive	consent
oral tradition	cultivate	rejected	encounter
legend	enemies	residents	reaction
character motive	political	assumed	beneficial
	violence	focus	interact
	carbon dioxide	individuals	partnership
	conservation	similarities	role
	native		
	nature		
	oxygen		
	symbiotic		

Put a check by the skills you can perform well. Review and practice any you haven't checked off. Check them off when you can perform them well.

Skills	I can . . .
Word Study	☐ spell words using *-s* blends. ☐ recognize and use the suffixes *-er* and *-or.* ☐ recognize and use synonyms. ☐ recognize sound-letter relationships.
Reading Strategies	☐ analyze cultural context. ☐ compare and contrast. ☐ identify with a character. ☐ classify.
Grammar	☐ use imperatives and embedded questions. ☐ use complex sentences. ☐ use transitions. ☐ recognize antecedent/pronoun agreement and parallel structure.
Writing	☐ write instructions. ☐ write a critique. ☐ write to compare and contrast. ☐ write a classifying paragraph. ☐ write an expository essay.

Copyright © by Pearson Education, Inc.

Test Preparation

DIRECTIONS
Read this selection. Then answer the questions that follow it.

The Red River War

1   In the mid-1800s, the United States <u>expanded</u> west. Native Americans living on land that belonged to the United States were forced to leave their homes. The tribes were moved to reservations. The reservations were not like the homes the Native Americans left behind. The government gave them food. They trained to be farmers. But this was not the life that many of the Native Americans wanted.

2   In 1874, some of the Native Americans were not on reservations. A few attacked a group of buffalo hunters in Texas. The army then declared war on all Native Americans who were not on reservations. Leaders of the tribes were sent to Florida. The Native Americans did not have leaders on the reservations. Soldiers hunted any Native American in the area. Native Americans were forced onto the reservations or killed.

3   In 1875, the army negotiated with the last group of Native Americans outside of the reservations. Their leader, Quanah Parker, led his people to Fort Sill, ending the war.

1 What is the purpose of the selection?
- **A**   To inform the reader about an important event
- **B**   To persuade the reader to visit Fort Sill
- **C**   To explain to the reader how to live in peace
- **D**   To describe to the reader life on the reservations

2 In the selection, what does <u>expanded</u> mean?
- **F**   lived
- **G**   hunted
- **H**   spread
- **J**   traveled

Copyright © by Pearson Education, Inc.

DIRECTIONS
Read this selection. Then answer the questions that follow it.

The Bald Eagle

1   The bald eagle is the national bird of the United States. This beautiful bird is the only eagle that is unique to North America. It is also one of the largest North American birds. Adult male eagles have a wingspan of about six and a half feet. The female eagles are even larger. They have a wingspan of about eight feet. They can fly at speeds of thirty miles per hour.

2   Eagles eat fish, other birds, and small mammals. They spot their <u>prey</u> from the air because they can see it from several hundred feet away. Then they dive to catch their food. They can dive as fast as 100 miles per hour. They grab their prey in their talons and fly away. They can lift prey that weighs about five pounds.

3   Eagles live for thirty years or more. Eagles also live in pairs and have the same partner for life. A pair of eagles builds a large nest in a big tree near a river or lake. Because the eagles add new material to their nest each year, a single nest may weigh up to 2,000 pounds.

1 What is paragraph 2 mainly about?
 A   The wingspan of bald eagles
 B   How bald eagles find and catch food
 C   Bald eagle nests
 D   Where to find bald eagles

2 According to the article, where do bald eagles build their nests?
 F   On cliffs
 G   In small trees
 H   In trees near the ocean
 J   In big trees

3 In paragraph 2, what words help the reader know what *prey* means?
 A   they spot
 B   from the air
 C   eat fish
 D   mile away

4 The author probably wrote this article to —
 A   persuade people to protect bald eagles
 B   give information about bald eagles
 C   explain how bald eagles became the national symbol
 D   give an opinion about bald eagles

Copyright © by Pearson Education, Inc.

TEST 3

DIRECTIONS
Read this selection. Then answer the questions that follow it.

Shirley and Jenny

1   Shirley, like many elephants transported overseas, has had a hard life. Shirley was born in the jungle of Indonesia in 1948. Five years later, she was captured and sold to a circus in the United States. She performed under the circus big top for more than twenty years. Then in 1975, when Shirley was twenty-eight, another elephant attacked her and broke one of her back legs. Her leg was not treated properly, and Shirley's recovery took many months. She could hardly walk. Shirley was sold to a zoo in Louisiana. It was a small zoo, and Shirley was the only elephant. She lived there for twenty-two years and had no contact with other elephants. In 1999, the zoo gave Shirley, now fifty-one, to the Elephant Sanctuary, a new 120-acre <u>sanctuary</u> in Tennessee. The Elephant Sanctuary is a place where people take care of neglected elephants.

2   On her first day at the sanctuary, Shirley did not want to go outside. A younger elephant named Jenny entered the stall next to Shirley's. Through the bars separating the stalls, Jenny and Shirley touched trunks. Immediately Jenny and Shirley became very excited and started to roar. When the sanctuary staff opened the gate between the stalls, Shirley and Jenny comforted each other for a long time. Then Jenny led Shirley out into the green pastures of the sanctuary. From that moment, the two elephants were always together.

3   The staff at the Elephant Sanctuary searched the records and discovered that Shirley and Jenny had worked together in the circus when Jenny first arrived in the United States. They had been together for only a few months, but during that time they became attached to each other. Perhaps Shirley had been like a mother to the five-year-old Jenny. After more than twenty years apart, they were finally together again.

Copyright © by Pearson Education, Inc.

1 Look at the timeline below.

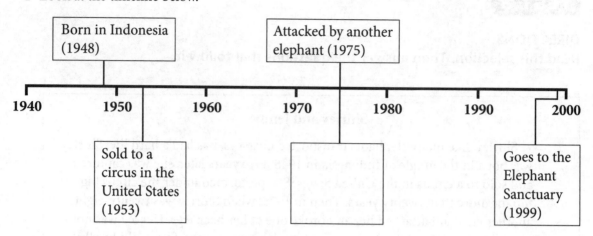

Which of the following belongs in the box?

A   Performed under the big top
B   Sold to a zoo in Louisiana
C   Transported to the United States
D   Meets Jenny

2 Paragraph 2 is mainly about —

F   Shirley's life in the circus
G   Shirley's reluctance to go outside
H   the reunion of Shirley and Jenny
J   the sanctuary staff

3 In paragraph 1, what words help the reader know what sanctuary means?

A   a place
B   in Tennessee
C   take care
D   120-acre

4 The reader can conclude that Shirley —

F   will miss performing in the circus
G   will continue to be happy at the sanctuary
H   will become upset at the sanctuary
J   will miss Jenny

5 Which sentence in paragraph 5 shows that Shirley was happy to see Jenny?

A   A younger elephant named Jenny entered the stall next to Shirley's.
B   Immediately Jenny and Shirley became very excited and started to roar.
C   Through the bars separating the stalls, Jenny and Shirley touched trunks.
D   Then Jenny led Shirley out into the green pastures of the sanctuary.

Copyright © by Pearson Education, Inc.

Visual Literacy: Smithsonian American
Art Museum *Use with textbook pages 228–229.*

LEARNING TO LOOK

Look at *Placa/Rollcall* by Charles "Chaz" Bojórquez on page 229 in your textbook.
The artist uses shapes in place of letters in this painting. Find the shapes and then
list as many as you can. State facts, not opinions.

Example: _____ *triangle* _____

1. _____   4. _____

2. _____   5. _____

3. _____   6. _____

INTERPRETATION

Look at *Merce C* by Franz Kline on page 228 in your textbook. Imagine that each of
the brushstrokes in the painting is a dancer. Describe his or her movements.

Example: ___ *The brushstroke on the right looks like it is moving an arm.* ___

_____

_____

_____

_____

_____

_____

What sounds or music is the dancer dancing to? Explain your answer.

_____

_____

Copyright © by Pearson Education, Inc.

Look at *Placa/Rollcall* by Charles "Chaz" Bojórquez again. If you could interview Chaz's friends, whose names appear in his artwork, what would you ask them? Use questions that begin with *Who, Where, When, What, Why,* and *How.*

Example: Where *did you grow up?*

7. Who _____

_____

8. Where _____

_____

9. When _____

_____

10. What _____

_____

11. Why _____

_____

12. How _____

_____

Copyright © by Pearson Education, Inc.

Name _____ Date _____

UNIT 4

What does home mean?

READING 1: "97 Orchard Street" / "The Pros and Cons of Tenement Life"

VOCABULARY   **Key Words** *Use with textbook page 233.*

Write each word in the box next to its definition.

exhibit	inspectors	mission	~~neighborhood~~	preserved	tenement

Example: *neighborhood* : a small area of town

1. _____: an assignment or purpose

2. _____: apartment house in a poor area of a city

3. _____: something shown to the public

4. _____: kept from harm or change

5. _____: officials who examine things carefully

Use the words in the box at the top of the page to complete the sentences.

6. The museum's _____ is to tell the story of the old town.

7. We visited an art gallery where a new _____ was on display.

8. The _____ looked around and said the wiring was safe.

9. The residents of the _____ were proud of their new library.

10. The family from China _____ many old Chinese traditions.

Copyright © by Pearson Education, Inc.

Read the paragraph below. Pay attention to the underlined academic words.

Heirlooms are <u>items</u> that are passed down from one family member to another. One <u>benefit</u> of keeping this tradition alive is that heirlooms give children of <u>immigrants</u> a connection to their ancestors' country. The design of the heirloom usually tells something about the <u>cultural</u> background it came from. For example, people in an Irish <u>community</u> sometimes wear a ring called a Claddagh. The ring is usually passed down from parents to their children. The ring shows two hands holding a heart, with a crown on top. These are symbols of ancient Ireland.

Write the letter of the correct definition next to each word.

Example: ___*b*___ cultural

_____ **1.** immigrants	**a.** people who enter another country in order to live there
_____ **2.** benefit	**b.** relating to a particular society and its way of life
_____ **3.** community	**c.** all the people living in one place
_____ **4.** items	**d.** things in a set, group, or list
	e. something that helps you or gives you an advantage

Use the academic words from the exercise above to complete the sentences.

5. The _____ were happy in their adopted country.

6. The annual parade brought together people in the _____.

7. One _____ of a balanced diet is more energy.

8. I inherited several _____ from my grandfather.

Complete the sentences with your own ideas.

Example: Most of the immigrants in my community are from ___*Haiti*___.

9. My most treasured items are _____.

10. One benefit of living in a diverse community is _____.

Copyright © by Pearson Education, Inc.

WORD STUDY   Silent Letters *Use with textbook page 235.*

REMEMBER The letters *gn, bt, mb,* and *kn* stand for one sound, not two. For example: the *g* is silent in *gnome*, the *b* is silent in *indebted*, the *b* is silent in *plumber*, and the *k* is silent in *knead*. Knowing when letters are silent will help you spell and pronounce words correctly.

Read the words in the box below. Then write each word in the correct column in the chart.

| designing | knowledge | crumb | gnarled | knack | undoubted |
| plumber | doubt | doubted | knob | thumb | gnaw |

Words with *gn*	Words with *bt*	Words with *mb*	Words with *kn*
designing			

Identify and write the silent letter in each word below.

Example: knoll _____ *silent k* _____

1. gnat   _____

2. assign   _____

3. doubtful   _____

4. knot   _____

5. tomb   _____

6. reign   _____

7. knitting   _____

8. bomb   _____

9. knee   _____

Copyright © by Pearson Education, Inc.

REMEMBER Visuals are the art, photographs, diagrams, charts, and maps that can come with a text. You can use visuals to learn more about the topic.

Look at the pictures and the text and answer the questions that follow.

About 12 million immigrants entered the United States through Ellis Island between 1892 and 1954. Roughly one-half of Americans have at least one ancestor who passed through here.

First- and second-class passengers did not have to go through Ellis Island. They were inspected aboard ship. If they were healthy and didn't have legal problems, they left when the ship docked. Third-class passengers, like Leonardo DiCaprio's character in *Titanic*, had to go to Ellis Island to have physical, mental, and legal examinations.

The chart shows that 1907 was Ellis Island's busiest year. The busiest day was April 17, 1907, when 11,747 immigrants arrived. After World War I, the United States opened embassies around the world, where people filled out forms and had medical exams before traveling. In November 1954, the last person left Ellis Island. In September 1990, the main building reopened as a museum. About two million people visit every year.

Year	Number of People Entering Ellis Island
1892	445,987
1898	178,748
1907	1,004,756
1919	26,731
1924	315,587

(Source: Annual Reports of the Commissioner General of Immigration, 1892–1924. Washington, D.C.)

1. What do you think the article is about ? _____

2. How does the picture help you understand the text? _____

_____

3. How does the chart help you understand the text? _____

_____

4. What is one interesting thing you learned from the information given? _____

_____

5. How do you think the skill of using visuals can help you understand the text?

_____

Copyright © by Pearson Education, Inc.

Name _____ Date _____

Choose the best answer for each item. Circle the letter of the correct answer.

1. The museum at 97 Orchard Street in New York City allows visitors to _____.

   a. meet people who grew up at that address
   b. see the immigrant experience firsthand
   c. do the same work that immigrants did in factories

2. The museum shares immigrant history by presenting _____.

   a. audio lectures
   b. apartments of immigrants from long ago
   c. movies and books

3. The nation's most famous gateway for immigrants was at _____.

   a. the Lower East Side
   b. the Upper West Side
   c. Staten Island

4. In the early 1900s, new immigrants found social support and assistance in _____.

   a. their home countries
   b. their jobs
   c. fraternal groups

5. Tenement life created many _____.

   a. cultural problems
   b. health problems
   c. financial problems

EXTENSION *Use with textbook page 241.*

Research five groups of immigrants that came to America. Find out where they settled in large numbers and what neighborhoods they formed there. Write the groups and the names of their new neighborhoods on the chart below.

Immigrant Group	Neighborhoods
Italians	Little Italy (NYC), North End (Boston)

Copyright © by Pearson Education, Inc.

Use with textbook page 242.

> **REMEMBER** An adjectival clause beginning with a relative pronoun describes a noun in an independent clause. A nonrestrictive adjectival clause gives extra information and is set off with commas. A restrictive adjectival clause is necessary to understand the antecedent to which it refers and is not set off with commas. When the relative pronoun is the subject of the adjectival clause, use *who* to refer to a person, *that* to refer to a thing in a restrictive clause, and *which* to refer to a thing in a nonrestrictive clause.
> **Example:** My new Prius, *which is parked over there*, was hit by a red car *that fled the scene of the accident.*

Circle the correct relative pronoun in each sentence below.

Example: People ((who)/which) travel are called tourists.

1. People (who / which) arrive in New York City by ship see the Statue of Liberty.

2. The statue, (that / which) is in Lafayette Park, was made by Berge.

3. The man (who / which) designed the statue was French.

4. Visitors explore the city, (who / which) has dozens of neighborhoods.

5. They travel on trains (who / that) run underground.

Circle the correct subject relative pronoun. Then complete each sentence with your own ideas.

Example: My mom's stories, ((which)/ that) ___are always about our family___, are my favorite.

6. The people (who / which) live in my neighborhood _____.

7. My favorite book, (who / which) sits on my shelf, _____.

8. My best friend, (who / that) lives _____, _____.

9. The immigrants (who / which) came to this country a hundred years ago _____

   _____.

10. The homes (who / that) were built a hundred years ago _____

   _____.

Copyright © by Pearson Education, Inc.

Adjectival Clauses: Object Relative Pronouns *Use with textbook page 243.*

> **REMEMBER** When a relative pronoun is the object of the adjectival clause, use *whom* to refer to people, *that* (in restrictive clauses) and *which* (in nonrestrictive clauses) to refer to things, *where* to refer to places, *when* to refer to times, and *whose* to show possession. Object relative pronouns come at the beginning of the clause. Be sure to use commas with nonrestrictive clauses.
> **Example:** The Darjeeling Café, *where we went for my birthday*, has closed down.

Complete the sentences with *whom, that, which, where, when,* or *whose*.

Example: The woman _____ *whom* _____ I met at the play called me.

1. We are staying in Astoria, _____ my friend lives.

2. A visitor can take a tour, _____ volunteers give.

3. The tours usually end at 5:00 P.M., _____ the museum closes.

4. The tour guide _____ I saw earlier is leaving.

Write each pair of sentences as one using the correct object relative pronoun.

Example: The salesclerk was very rude. I waited in her line.

   The salesclerk whose line I waited in was very rude.

5. The concert was great. It ended late.

   _____.

6. I told you about the movie. I saw it last night.

   _____.

7. Denmark is in northern Europe. I've always wanted to go to Denmark.

   _____.

8. My only brother is graduating tomorrow. You met him last night.

   _____.

Copyright © by Pearson Education, Inc.

Complete your own 5Ws chart for a magazine article about an event in your town.

Who?	
What?	
Where?	
When?	
Why?	

Use the Peer Review Checklist below to obtain feedback from your partner.
This feedback will help you edit your final draft.

PEER REVIEW CHECKLIST

☐ Does the first sentence introduce the topic?

☐ Does the paragraph answer the 5W questions about the topic?

☐ Does the writer grab the reader's attention with interesting information?

☐ Is the vocabulary appropriate to the topic?

☐ Are adjectival clauses used correctly?

☐ What changes could be made to improve the article?

Copyright © by Pearson Education, Inc.

Name _____ Date _____

UNIT 4

What does home mean?

READING 2: "Somebody's Son"

VOCABULARY **Literary Words** *Use with textbook page 247.*

REMEMBER **Suspense** is a feeling of uncertainty about the outcome of a story. It makes readers wonder what will happen next. Most stories build to a **climax**, or moment of highest intensity. It is often the most suspenseful moment of a story.

Read each situation. Write *yes* if it builds suspense. Write *no* if it does not.

Suspenseful?	Situation
no	Marguerite poured herself a glass of milk and drank it slowly.
1.	Alistair stepped off the plane. The person waiting for him was someone he would never have expected.
2.	The policeman drank his cup of coffee slowly. He loved the taste of hot coffee first thing in the morning.
3.	The door was open just a crack. Through the crack, we could see a figure with a flashlight searching the room. But who could it be?

Write one or two sentences describing each situation. Try to build suspense with your choice of words and details.

Situation	Sentence
a student is running out of time	*The other students were finishing their tests, but Matilda had barely begun the last question. She looked down at the paper and started to panic.*
4. a camper is lost in the woods	
5. two friends enter a foot race	

Copyright © by Pearson Education, Inc.

Read the paragraph below. Pay attention to the underlined academic words.

> At our school, the principal's office can <u>correspond</u> with students and their parents through e-mail. We might get a message that our <u>transportation</u> to school will be delayed on a certain day. Or if a snowstorm or some other extreme weather event <u>occurs</u>, a message will <u>indicate</u> that we should not go to school that day.

Write the academic words from the paragraph above next to their correct definitions.

Example: _____*occurs*_____: happens

1. _____: write to someone and receive letters from him or her

2. _____: the process or business of moving people or goods from one place to another

3. _____: say or do something that shows what you want or intend to do

Use the academic words from the paragraph above to complete the sentences.

4. A lunar eclipse, where the moon is in the earth's shadow, _____ twice a year.

5. The bus broke down, so the players needed other _____ to get to the game.

6. Please _____ that you know the answer by raising your hand.

7. I frequently _____ with my grandmother by writing long letters.

Complete the sentences with your own ideas.

Example: If I could, I would correspond with _*Isaac Newton.*_____

8. My favorite mode of transportation is _____

9. Something that occurs every day at my school is _____

10. I often indicate how I feel by _____

Copyright © by Pearson Education, Inc.

WORD STUDY **Homophones** *Use with textbook page 249.*

REMEMBER Homophones are words that sound the same but are spelled differently and have different meanings. For example, *I, aye,* and *eye* are homophones. *I* means "me"; *aye* means "yes"; and *eye* means "the part of your face that you see with." When you use or read a homophone and are unsure of its meaning and part of speech, look it up in a dictionary.

Write your own definitions for each pair of homophones in the chart. Then check your definitions in a dictionary.

Homophones	Definitions
Example: ad, add	*advertisement, to total*
1. heir, air	
2. bald, bawled	
3. barren, baron	
4. steel, steal	
5. tease, teas	

Write definitions for each pair of homophones below. Use a dictionary if necessary. Then use both words in sentences that show their meanings. You can write a sentence for each word or use both words in one sentence.

Example: tense, tents _*nervous; canvas housing structure*_
*The kids feel tense when they are camping in tents and see bears coming!*

6. bazaar, bizarre _____

_____

7. threw, through _____

_____

8. sighs, size _____

_____

9. leak, leek _____

_____

Copyright © by Pearson Education, Inc.

REMEMBER To summarize, find the main ideas and state them in a few short sentences. Leave out details and focus on the most important points.

Read each passage. Then answer the questions that follow.

There are many ways to travel between New York City and Boston. You can take the fast train, which takes 3 ½ hours. You can take the bus, which takes about 4 hours. You can drive in your own car, which takes about 4 hours. You can take a plane, which takes just 1 hour.

1. Summarize the passage above in one sentence.

_____

2. Which details did you leave out of your summary?

_____

Homes come in all kinds of shapes and sizes. Igloos are homes made of ice and snow. Log cabins are homes made of wood. Many homes in cities are tall apartment buildings made of steel and concrete. Whatever type of home a person has, all that really matters is that it feels safe and warm.

3. Summarize the passage above in one sentence.

_____

4. What details did you leave out of your summary?

_____

5. How can the strategy of summarizing help you to better understand what you read?

_____

Copyright © by Pearson Education, Inc.

COMPREHENSION   *Use with textbook page 256.*

Choose the best answer for each item. Circle the letter of the correct answer.

1. David wrote to his parents to let them know he was _____.

   a. in Baltimore   **b.** hitchhiking home   **c.** going to college

2. To show that it was acceptable for him to come home, he asked that his dad _____.

   a. meet him at the   **b.** leave a scarecrow   **c.** tie a white cloth
       train station   by a tree   to a tree

3. Suspense builds in the story every time David _____.

   a. is delayed on his trip   **b.** checks his mail   **c.** falls asleep and nearly
       misses his stop

4. The story's climax comes when the train passenger _____.

   a. goes to college   **b.** sees the apple tree   **c.** boards the train

5. At the end of the story David finds out that _____.

   a. his father wants to   **b.** he isn't welcome   **c.** his parents never
       see him   at home   got the letter

RESPONSE TO LITERATURE   *Use with textbook page 257.*

Reread the last line of the story. Then write a short paragraph describing how you think David felt when he heard about the tree.

_____

_____

_____

_____

_____

Copyright © by Pearson Education, Inc.

Use with textbook page 258.

> **REMEMBER** An adjective or adjectival phrase modifies, or describes, a noun or noun phrase. It usually comes before the noun it describes or after a linking verb. A prepositional phrase can also function as an adjective; if follows the adjective it modifies.

Underline the adjective(s) or adjectival phrase in each sentence. Circle the noun or noun phrase that is modified.

Example: (The woman) from our office is tall and beautiful.

1. We picked wild mushrooms from the forest.

2. A slim, elegant woman entered the room.

3. The movie about the dog was wonderful.

4. John is a young man full of ideas.

Answer each question using the adjectival phrase in parentheses.

Example: How was the movie? (sad but interesting)

    It was sad but interesting.

5. What kind of person is he? (nice, thoughtful)

    _____.

6. What kind of dancer is she? (talented and graceful)

    _____.

7. How was the movie? (boring without much plot)

    _____.

8. What kind of cheese is this? (goat, from Switzerland)

    _____.

Copyright © by Pearson Education, Inc.

Adverbs and Adverbial Phrases *Use with textbook page 259.*

> **REMEMBER** An adverb or adverbial phrase modifies a verb, an adjective, or another adverb. Many adverbs that modify verbs are formed by adding -*ly* to an adjective.
> A prepositional phrase can also modify a verb, telling place and time.
> **Example:** She doesn't *usually* work *at the hospital on Saturdays*.
> A qualifier is a type of adverb that modifies another adverb or adjective. Adverbs can appear in numerous places in a sentence, but qualifiers like *quite*, *very*, *rather*, etc. appear before the word they modify.
> **Example:** He walked *rather quickly* because he was *very* happy to see me.

Underline the adverb(s) or adverbial phrase(s) in each sentence. Circle the verb, adjective, or adverb that is modified.

Example: The girl <u>patiently</u> (waited) <u>in the car</u>.

1. He politely opened the door.

2. The man walked quickly to the shop.

3. He marched very proudly in the parade.

4. They lived happily in Canada for many years.

Insert the adverb(s) or adverbial phrase(s) correctly into each sentence. More than one answer may be possible.

Example: She danced. (gracefully, in the moonlight)
  gracefully   in the moonlight

5. She reacted to the news. (quite calmly)

6. Joan arrived. (finally, at the cafe)

7. Butch buys stamps. (very often, downtown)

8. A tall woman entered the room. (rather, quietly)

Copyright © by Pearson Education, Inc.

Complete your own plot summary chart for a story from a book, film, or television show you know well.

Characters	
Setting	
Conflict	
Main events	
Resolution	

Use the Peer Review Checklist below to obtain feedback from your partner. This feedback will help you edit your final draft.

PEER REVIEW CHECKLIST

☐ Does the paragraph include only the main points?

☐ Does the paragraph describe the characters, the setting, and the main events of the story?

☐ Does the paragraph explain the main conflict and the resolution of the story?

☐ Are adjectives and adverbs included?

☐ Are adjectival and adverbial phrases included?

☐ What changes could be made to improve the paragraph?

Copyright © by Pearson Education, Inc.

What does home mean?

READING 3: *The Lotus Seed*

VOCABULARY **Literary Words** *Use with textbook page 263.*

> **REMEMBER** The **speaker** of a poem is the character who tells the poem. A **symbol** is anything that stands for something else. It has its own meaning, but can also stand for an idea or feeling.

Read each sentence. Write whether it contains a symbol or a line of a poem narrated by a speaker.

Sense	Description
speaker	*I think you're like a summer day, / Please listen and I'll count the ways*
1.	We stand watching / leaves falling in autumn
2.	The statue represented happiness.
3.	Do you remember the smell of evening? / We shared it, smiling

Read the two poems below. Circle the clues that help you determine who the speaker is. Then write who the speaker is. The first clue has been circled.

(When I was ten-and-three) I'm certain I did see A tiny brontosaurus I'm sure it said to me "I live beneath a certain tree Right here, deep in the forest" Dear grandson, this is true! It might happen to you . . . 4. _____	We float above waiting, Rumble and light, High overhead. Gather and burst Then tumble and down, Splatter and splash We pool at your feet And race down your rivers And dampen your hair. How else would we meet? 5. _____

Copyright © by Pearson Education, Inc.

Read the paragraph below. Pay attention to the underlined academic words.

> My grandmother <u>removed</u> the ruby ring she was wearing and showed it to me. She said, "I'm very <u>attached</u> to this ring. My own grandmother gave it to me." I looked closely at the small, but very beautiful ring. By my grandmother's smile, I could see that the ring was a <u>source</u> of great pleasure for her. "A ruby can <u>symbolize</u> love," she said.

Write the academic words from the paragraph above next to their correct definitions.

Example: _____*source*_____: where something comes from

1. _____: represent a quality or feeling

2. _____: emotionally connected to

3. _____: took something away from where it was

Use the academic words from the paragraph above to complete the sentences.

4. On the American flag, the stars _____ the 50 states.

5. The thief _____ the jewel from the glass case.

6. The puppies were _____ to their mother right away.

7. The _____ of the quotation is from a book that I read years ago.

Complete the sentences with your own ideas.

Example: Children grow very attached to ___*their pets*_____.

8. Doves often symbolize _____.

9. The source of my motivation is _____.

10. When I get home, I usually remove _____.

Copyright © by Pearson Education, Inc.

WORD STUDY **Spelling Long *o*** *Use with textbook page 265.*

REMEMBER The long *o* sound can be spelled several different ways. These include *o* as in *cold*, *oa* as in *roast*, *o_e* as in *bone*, and *ow* as in *show*. Knowing these sound-spelling relationships will help you spell and say words with long *o* correctly.

Read the words in the box below. Then write each word in the correct column in the chart.

~~pagoda~~	moan	swallow	zone	toast	snow
aglow	loaf	hello	vote	ago	telephone

Words with long *o* spelled *o*	Words with long *o* spelled *oa*	Words with long *o* spelled *o_e*	Words with long *o* spelled *ow*
pagoda			

For each word below, write the letter or letters that stand for the long *o* sound.

Example: colt ___*long o spelled o*___

1. boast _____

2. hold _____

3. strove _____

4. row _____

5. float _____

6. unknown _____

7. grown _____

8. nowhere _____

9. tone _____

Copyright © by Pearson Education, Inc.

Use with textbook page 265.

> **REMEMBER** When you read, analyze text structure by studying the way the parts of a text are arranged. Remember that poems and plays have a special text structure. They are arranged in lines and groups of lines called stanzas. Narrative poems are written in verse. Punctuation doesn't always follow the same rules in poetry as it does in other types of text.

Read each passage below. Then answer the questions that follow each passage.

Every day
In every way
I try to grow
Strong and proud

1. What is the text structure of the passage above?

_____

2. Are there rhyming lines in the passage above? If so, what are they?

_____

KIM:　We have to solve the mystery!
JUAN: I told you already. It's too dangerous!
KIM:　If we don't solve it, who will?
JUAN: Promise me that one day, you'll stop dragging me into your adventures!
KIM:　Does that mean you'll help me solve the mystery?
JUAN: I guess I have no choice.

3. What is the text structure of the passage above?

_____

4. What do the words in bold represent in this text structure?

_____

5. How can the strategy of analyzing text structure help you become a better reader?

_____

Copyright © by Pearson Education, Inc.

COMPREHENSION *Use with textbook page 270.*

Choose the best answer for each item. Circle the letter of the correct answer.

1. The speaker's grandmother takes the lotus seed in order to _____.

   a. give it to her grandchildren

   b. remember the emperor

   c. remember Vietnam

2. When the grandmother's family left the country, she _____.

   a. took the lotus seed

   b. took her hair combs

   c. took water from the River of Perfume

3. For the grandmother, the lotus seed symbolizes _____.

   a. a new life in the United States

   b. the old ways in Vietnam

   c. the Vietnam War

4. When Bà sees the lotus blossom growing in her garden, she feels _____.

   a. remorse

   b. anger

   c. hope

5. The seed allows the speaker to _____.

   a. connect her life to her grandmother's life in Vietnam

   b. plant her own garden

   c. see the golden dragon throne of the emperor

RESPONSE TO LITERATURE *Use with textbook page 271.*

In *The Lotus Seed*, the seed acts as a symbol for the grandmother. Think of your own family and your heritage. What symbol would you choose to represent your memories and traditions? Write a short paragraph describing this symbol.

_____

_____

_____

_____

_____

REMEMBER Adverbial clauses of time are subordinate, or dependent, clauses that express *when* and are used with a main, or independent clause. Adverbial clauses begin with subordinating conjunctions (*after, before, when, while, as soon as, by the time, until, whenever*). Each of these shows a different time order. For example, *as soon as* and *by the time* imply that the action in the adverbial clause must be finished before the second action can happen. *Until* implies an action in the future. *When* is often used with a clause in the simple form; *while* is often used with a clause in the progressive form.

Underline the adverbial clause in each sentence. Circle the subordinating conjunction.

Example: We went out to dinner (when) my father got home.

1. Whenever my aunt visits, we get presents.

2. I plan to be a doctor after I graduate.

3. As soon as you know the answer, raise your hand.

4. You can't go until you finish your homework.

5. The caterpillar will turn into a butterfly by the time it matures.

Complete the sentences with information about yourself.

Example: _____I usually read a book_____ whenever it rains.

6. When we don't have school, _____.

7. _____ after school lets out for summer.

8. As soon as I save enough money, _____.

9. By the time I'm 25, _____.

10. _____ while I was doing my homework.

Copyright © by Pearson Education, Inc.

Adverbial Clauses of Purpose, Reason, and Contrast

Use with textbook page 273.

> **REMEMBER** An adverbial clause, like other adverbs, can modify the action of a sentence. To express the purpose of an action, use the subordinating conjunctions *in order that* or *so that*. To express the reason for an action, use *because*, *since*, or *as*. To contrast two actions, use *although*, *even though*, or *though*.
> When an adverbial clause begins a sentence, it is followed by a comma.

Underline the adverbial clause in each sentence. Write whether it is an adverbial clause of *purpose*, *reason*, or *contrast*.

Example: He couldn't swim <u>since it was winter</u>. _____*reason*_____

1. Although he enjoyed his vacation, he was ready to go home. _____

2. Marty built a tree house so that he would have his own private place.

_____

3. As it was almost noon, the teacher postponed our test. _____

4. In order that we could leave early, my father left work at three. _____

Combine the pairs of sentences with an appropriate subordinating conjunction. More than one answer is possible.

Example: Sharon came home early. She was having a good time.

   Sharon came home early even though she was having a good time.

5. I joined the soccer team. I could get into shape.

_____.

6. Jessica took off her sweater. It was warm inside the house.

_____.

7. He likes sports cars. He likes to drive fast.

_____.

8. School usually begins in September. This year, it began in August.

_____.

Copyright © by Pearson Education, Inc.

Use with textbook pages 274–275.

Complete your own idea web for a response to a story or another piece of literature.

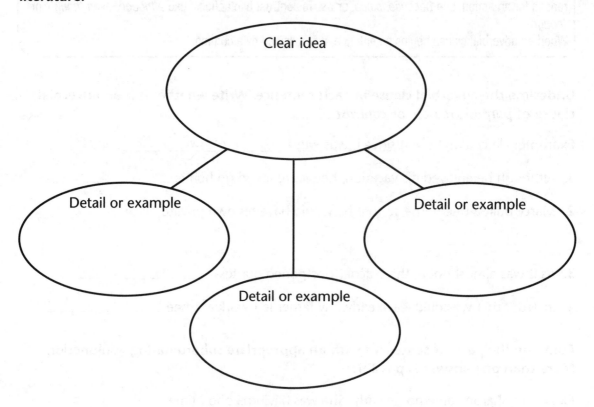

Clear idea

Detail or example

Detail or example

Detail or example

Use the Peer Review Checklist below to obtain feedback from your partner. This feedback will help you edit your final draft.

PEER REVIEW CHECKLIST

☐ Does the paragraph explain the main idea of the story or poem?

☐ Does the paragraph explain how the main idea is developed through the details of the story or poem?

☐ Are the statements supported with evidence from the text?

☐ Is the paragraph clearly organized?

☐ Are adverbial clauses of time used correctly?

☐ Are adverbial clauses of purpose, reason, and contrast used correctly?

☐ What changes could be made to improve the paragraph?

Copyright © by Pearson Education, Inc.

UNIT 4

What does home mean?

READING 4: "Operation Migration"

VOCABULARY   **Key Words** *Use with textbook page 277.*

Write each word in the box next to its definition.

endangered species	migration	monitor	population	rare	refuge

Example: ___*migration*___ : the movement of animals from one region to another

1. _____: the number of animals or people living in an area

2. _____: not seen or found very often

3. _____: carefully watch for changes

4. _____: a safe place set aside for people or animals

5. _____: a kind of animal whose numbers are so small it risks becoming extinct

Use the words in the box at the top of the page to complete the sentences.

6. Most of the _____ of that species is found in Asia.

7. That bird is an _____, and there are not many left.

8. The scientists will _____ that group of baboons for six months.

9. The monarch butterfly _____ is a beautiful sight.

10. The bald eagle was once a very _____ bird.

Copyright © by Pearson Education, Inc.

Read the paragraph below. Pay attention to the underlined academic words.

Last week we had a <u>substitute</u> teacher. She asked us to get into groups and discuss the meaning of the last reading assignment. She walked around to listen as we discussed. She took an unusual <u>route</u> through the classroom, so we didn't know which group she would visit next. After we finished, she asked us to write a paragraph about the <u>outcome</u> of our discussions. The earlier <u>interaction</u> with my group helped me write my paragraph.

Write the letter of the correct definition next to each word.

Example: __c__ outcome

_____ 1. substitute

_____ 2. route

_____ 3. interaction

a. the activity of talking with other people and working together with them

b. someone who does someone else's job

c. the final result of a meeting, process, etc.

d. the way from one place to another

Use the academic words from the exercise above to complete the sentences.

4. The teacher took notes on the _____ between the two children.

5. Migrating reindeer use the same _____ every year in search of food.

6. The process was different whenever we worked together, but the _____ was always the same.

7. When our teacher was sick, a _____ taught our class for the day.

Complete the sentences with your own ideas.

Example: The easiest route to the ocean is ___*along the river.*___

8. My interaction with the principal is always _____

9. My favorite substitute teacher is _____

10. You can change the outcome of a situation by _____

Copyright © by Pearson Education, Inc.

WORD STUDY   Suffix *-ion* *Use with textbook page 279.*

REMEMBER A suffix is a letter or group of letters added to the end of a base word to make a new word. Adding suffixes to base words usually changes the word's part of speech and meaning. The suffix *-ion*, for example, means "an act or process" and makes a verb into a noun. For nouns that end in silent *e*, drop the *e* before adding *-ion*, as in *elevate* and *elevation*.

Look at the chart below. Add the suffix *-ion* to create a new word. Write the new word on the chart. Then write the meaning of the new word. Notice how the part of speech of the word changes when you add *-ion*.

Base Word (verb)	Suffix	New Word (noun)	Definition
educate	-ion	*education*	*schooling*
1. adopt	-ion		
2. motivate	-ion		
3. attract	-ion		
4. eliminate	-ion		
5. depress	-ion		

Create a noun by adding the suffix *-ion* to each verb below. Then write a sentence with the noun.

Verb	Noun	Sentence
Example: inform	*information*	*I need some information about sandhill cranes.*
6. delete		
7. confuse		
8. correct		
9. protect		
10. translate		

Copyright © by Pearson Education, Inc.

Use with textbook page 279.

> **REMEMBER** You can monitor comprehension by rereading a text. Make a list of difficult words. Try to figure out their meanings from the context, or look them up in a dictionary. Then restate the information in your own words.

Read each passage. Then answer the questions and follow directions.

Every Christmas, I visit my grandparents in Maine. We have stayed with them for Christmas every year since I was a little girl. We pack up the family car with presents and suitcases. Then we drive hundreds and hundreds of miles from our home in Virginia to Maine. The trip begins early in the morning and we reach my grandparents' house in time for dinner. When we get there, my grandparents have their Christmas tree decorated with lights. We sing carols and put our presents under the tree. The countryside is almost always covered with beautiful, white snow. I love Christmas in Maine.

1. Are there any difficult words in the passage? If so, write them down. Try to figure out their meanings from the context, or look them up in a dictionary.

   _____

2. What is the passage about?

   _____

I feel very strongly that high school students should have less homework. Most of us work an after-school job every day to earn pocket money. By the time we get home and have dinner, we're exhausted. We just want to relax, watch some TV, talk with our friends, and go to bed. We do not have the energy to take out our school books and spend an hour or two on homework.

3. Are there any difficult words in the passage? If so, write them down. Try to figure out their meanings from the context, or look them up in a dictionary.

   _____

4. What is the passage about?

   _____

   _____

5. How can the strategy of monitoring comprehension help you become a better reader?

   _____

Name _____ Date _____

Choose the best answer for each item. Circle the letter of the correct answer.

1. The whooping cranes became endagered because of the _____.

   a. whooping crane   **b.** expansion of American   **c.** explosion in the
      disease   cities   domestic cat population

2. The goal of Operation Migration is to _____.

   a. produce a second   **b.** raise awareness of   **c.** train birds to
      migratory flock   endangered species   trust humans

3. Sandhill cranes were used to test Operation Migration because there are _____.

   a. only a few of them   **b.** many of them   **c.** people who like them

4. The flight of the sandhill cranes behind the ultralight took _____.

   a. as long as cranes   **b.** much longer than   **c.** much less time than
      flying alone   cranes flying alone   cranes flying alone

5. Whooping cranes are still in danger because _____.

   a. humans hunt them   **b.** there are only 15 left   **c.** all whooping cranes
      for sport   in the world   are part of one
                                       single flock

Research five endangered species. On the table below, write the remaining population for each species and where it is found. Then mark each animal's territory on a map.

Species	Population	Habitat
Hawaiian duck	2,200	Hawaii

Copyright © by Pearson Education, Inc.

Factual Conditional in the Present and Future

Use with textbook page 286.

REMEMBER A factual conditional in the present shows a condition that is now true. Use the simple present both in the *if*-clause and in the result clause.
Examples: If it snows, we play outside. When it rains, we play inside.
A factual conditional in the future tells about a condition that might come true. Use the simple present in the *if*-clause. You can use *will*, *be going to*, or a present modal, such as *can*, *may*, or *might* in the result clause.
Example: If it snows today, we might not have school.

Underline the *if*-clause in each conditional sentence. Then write whether the conditional is *present factual* or *future factual*.

Example: You can go to the concert <u>if you finish your homework</u>. _____*future factual*_____

1. If I have enough time, I like to read in the evenings. _____

2. I might read tonight if I have enough time. _____

3. I always get hungry when I don't eat breakfast. _____

4. If I don't eat breakfast, I'll get hungry in class. _____

Draw a line to match the correct clause on the left with the clause on the right.

Example: Deb always answers the phone   he always comes.

5. I can fix your bike   if it meows.

6. If we have enough apples,   if she is in her office.

7. If you invite Tom,   if you have a spare tire.

8. Let the cat in   we can bake a cake.

Copyright © by Pearson Education, Inc.

Present and Past Unreal Conditional *Use with textbook page 287.*

> **REMEMBER** Present unreal conditionals tell about conditions that are presently untrue but could possibly still happen. Use the simple past in the *if*-clause; use a past modal, such as *would* or *could*, + the base form of the verb in the result clause.
> **Example:** If we *walked* more quickly, we *could catch* up.
> Past unreal conditionals tell about untrue conditions that are no longer possible. Use the past perfect in the *if*-clause; use a past modal + *have* + the past participle in the result clause.
> **Example:** If we *had walked* more quickly, we *might have caught* up.

Circle the result clause in each conditional sentence. Then write whether the conditional is *present unreal* or *past unreal*.

Example: If we get enough votes, (we could change the plan.) *present unreal* _____

1. If I'd had enough time, I would've sent you a postcard. _____

2. I would drive to school if I had a car. _____

3. If he had more money, he would travel around the world. _____

4. If we'd had a cat, we wouldn't have been able to go to the beach.

_____

Complete each unreal conditional with your own ideas.

Example: If I won the lottery, *I'd buy my family a big house.* _____

5. If I could speak English fluently, _____.

6. If I had started studying English earlier, _____.

7. If I could go anywhere in the world, _____.

8. If I had known _____, _____.

Copyright © by Pearson Education, Inc.

WRITING **Write a Problem-and-Solution Paragraph**

Use with textbook pages 288–289.

Complete your own problem-and-solution chart for a paragraph you write to describe a problem in your school and how it was solved.

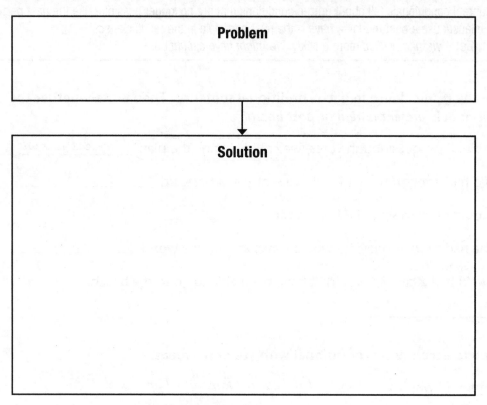

Use the Peer Review Checklist below to obtain feedback from your partner. This feedback will help you edit your final draft.

PEER REVIEW CHECKLIST

☐ Does the paragraph clearly explain the problem?

☐ Does the paragraph present a solution to the problem?

☐ Are the steps of the solution clearly explained?

☐ Are sequence words used to describe the steps?

☐ Are factual and unreal conditional sentences used correctly?

☐ Do subjects and verbs agree in number?

☐ What changes could be made to improve the paragraph?

Copyright © by Pearson Education, Inc.

Name _____ Date _____

WRITING WORKSHOP *Use with textbook pages 294–298.*

Organize your ideas in the graphic organizer below.

I.
   A.
   B.
II.
   A.
   B.
III.
   A.
   B.
IV.
   A.
   B.
V.
   A.
   B.

Use the Peer Review Checklist below to obtain feedback from your partner. This feedback will help you edit your final draft.

PEER REVIEW CHECKLIST

☐ Was the essay clearly organized?

☐ Was the information interesting?

☐ Did I understand the topic better after reading it?

☐ Did the first paragraph introduce the topic?

☐ Did the concluding paragraph sum up the main points?

☐ What changes could be made to improve the essay?

Underline the vocabulary items you know and can use well. Review and practice any you haven't underlined. Underline them when you know them well.

Literary Words	Key Words	Academic Words	
suspense	exhibit	benefit	attached
climax	inspectors	community	removed
speaker	mission	cultural	source
symbol	neighborhood	immigrants	symbolize
	preserved	items	interaction
	tenement	correspond	outcome
	accommodate	indicate	route
	catastrophe	occurs	substitute
	donating	transportation	
	identified		
	imminent		
	unsanitary		

Put a check by the skills you can perform well. Review and practice any you haven't checked off. Check them off when you can perform them well.

Skills	I can . . .
Word Study	☐ spell words with silent letters. ☐ recognize and use homophones. ☐ recognize and spell words with long *o*. ☐ recognize and use the suffix *-ion*.
Reading Strategies	☐ use visuals. ☐ summarize. ☐ analyze text structure. ☐ perform critical analyses.
Grammar	☐ use adjectival clauses. ☐ use adjectives and adverbs. ☐ use adverbial clauses. ☐ use factual and unreal conditional.
Writing	☐ write a magazine article. ☐ write a plot summary. ☐ write a response to a piece of literature. ☐ write a problem-and-solution paragraph. ☐ write an expository essay.

Test Preparation

DIRECTIONS
Read this selection. Then answer the questions that follow it.

Coming Home

1   Natalia and her family had a terrific vacation. Visiting family in Colombia is always fun. Natalia played with cousins she had not seen in years.

2   The long plane ride home made Natalia tired. Her little sister Anna whined and cried. Mother tried to quiet her. Father gave Anna candy. Nothing worked.

3   Anna curled up against Natalia's shoulder. Natalia talked softly to the girl. She told Anna that she should fall asleep. If she did, she could dream about home. Anna could play with her friends. She could play with her toys. Anna could dream of lying in bed with Natalia in their own bedroom.

4   All the talking made Natalia very sleepy. She <u>drifted off</u>, still holding Anna's hand. She had sweet dreams. Soon she heard Anna calling her name. They were finally home.

1 According to the passage, Natalia visited _____.
   A   her parents and sister
   B   cousins at the airport
   C   family in Colombia
   D   friends back home

2 In the selection, what does <u>drifted off</u> mean?
   F   floated away
   G   landed softly
   H   flew away
   J   fell asleep

Copyright © by Pearson Education, Inc.

DIRECTIONS
Read this selection. Then answer the questions that follow it.

Mammals

1   Mammals are animals that produce living young, feed their babies milk, and breathe using lungs. Humans, lions, and bears are examples of mammals. Most mammals make their home on land. For example, lions live in prairies, plains, and savannah grasslands. These large areas of land are covered with grasses and have very few trees or shrubs. Bears live in forests and woods. Some mammals, like whales and dolphins, make their home in water. They can be found in oceans around the world.

2   All mammals have fur or hair to keep them warm and protect their bodies. The amount of hair or fur they have depends on the <u>climate</u> of their home. Mammals that live in cold weather, such as polar bears, usually have a lot of fur or hair to keep them warm. Mammals that live in warmer climates often do not have as much hair because it takes less to keep their bodies warm. Elephants, whales, and humans are examples of mammals that don't have a lot of hair. In fact, whales have hair only on their face.

---

1 What is paragraph 1 mainly about?
  A   Where mammals live
  B   Where lions live
  C   Where whales live
  D   Where bears live

2 How did the author organize this article?
  F   The article defines mammals and explains why mammals have fur or hair.
  G   The article explains why mammals live on land and water. Then the article describes the amount of hair types of mammals have.
  H   The article defines mammals, describes where they live, and explains the amount of hair mammals have.
  J   The article compares and contrasts different kinds of mammals.

3 In paragraph 2, what word or words help the reader know what *climate* means?
  A   fur or hair
  B   cold weather
  C   their home
  D   polar bears

4 Why do elephants have less hair than polar bears?
  F   They live in a cold climate.
  G   They live on the plains.
  H   They do not need to keep warm.
  J   They live in a warm climate.

Copyright © by Pearson Education, Inc.

TEST 3

DIRECTIONS
Read this selection. Then answer the questions that follow it.

Taro and the Sea Dragon's Palace

1   Many years ago in a small village by the Sea of Japan, there lived a poor young fisherman named Taro Urashima. One day, Taro noticed some boys teasing a baby sea turtle with sticks and stones. Taro felt sorry for the turtle, so he rescued it and put it back into the ocean.

2   Some time later when Taro was fishing, a giant sea turtle <u>emerged</u> from the water. Taro was startled when he saw the turtle rise up from the ocean. The turtle thanked Taro for rescuing him and offered to take him to the Sea Dragon's Palace at the bottom of the sea so that Princess Oto might thank him, too. Never having seen the bottom of the sea, Taro agreed. He jumped onto the turtle's back, and they went deep into the ocean.

3   Taro and the turtle arrived at an enormous golden palace. The beautiful Princess Oto welcomed Taro inside. She had prepared a great feast with the most delicious food Taro had ever tasted. After dinner, the princess asked if Taro would like to stay at the palace. Taro agreed, and each day thereafter was filled with wonders and riches.

4   After some time, Taro began to feel homesick. The princess wept when he told her this, but Taro was determined to return home. As a parting gift, the princess gave Taro a jeweled box. She told him to always keep it with him but never to open it.

5   When Taro arrived back at his village, he didn't recognize any of the people. When he went to his parents' house, it wasn't there. He asked an old woman where the Urashima family could be found. She laughed and said the Urashima family had been gone for over a hundred years.

6   Sitting by the sea, very sad and confused, Taro looked at the box Princess Oto had given him. Forgetting her warning, he opened it. A huge cloud of green smoke came out. When the smoke cleared, Taro was an old man. He had been at the Sea Dragon's Palace for many, many years.

Copyright © by Pearson Education, Inc.

1 Which sentence from the selection shows that Taro is kind?

    A *After some time, Taro began to feel homesick.*

    B *He jumped onto the turtle's back, and then went deep into the ocean.*

    C *Taro felt sorry for the turtle, so he rescued it and put it back into the ocean.*

    D *One day, Taro noticed some boys teasing a baby sea turtle with sticks and stones.*

2 Paragraph 5 is mainly about —

    F how the village changed while Taro was in the sea

    G how the village had grown while Taro was in the sea

    H how the old lady reacted to Taro

    J where Taro's family home had gone

3 In paragraph 2, what words help the reader know what *emerged* means?

    A was startled

    B was fishing

    C rise up

    D some time later

4 The reader can conclude that before Taro opened the box —

    F he thought the box would help him find his family

    G he looked the same as the day he went into the sea

    H he wanted to return to the golden palace

    J he wanted to find out where his family had gone

5 In paragraph 2, the phrase "Never having seen the bottom of the sea" tells the reader that Taro —

    A is afraid of the ocean

    B likes to visit new places

    C has not been to the ocean before

    D does not like visiting new places

Visual Literacy: Smithsonian American
Art Museum *Use with textbook pages 300–301.*

Look at *Camas para Sueños* by Carmen Lomas Garza on page 300 in your textbook. Use that artwork to complete the web diagram below. For each "string" in the diagram, write a detail that you see. State facts, not opinions.

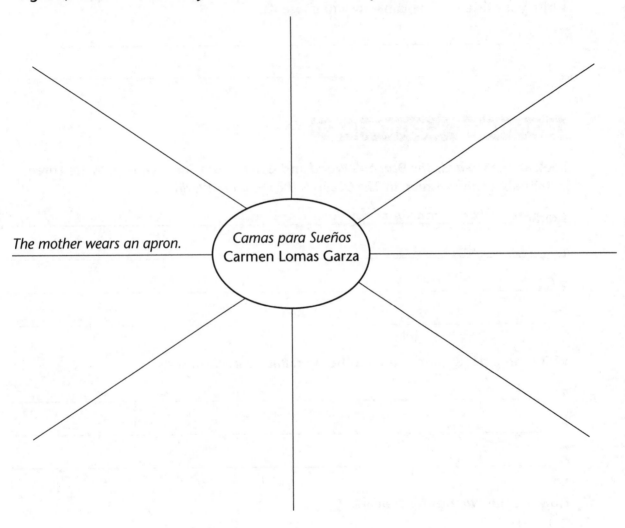

The mother wears an apron.

Camas para Sueños
Carmen Lomas Garza

Copyright © by Pearson Education, Inc.

Look at *The Ocean Is the Dragon's World* by Hung Liu on page 301 in your textbook. What title would you give Hung Liu's painting?

Example: *I would call this painting* <u>*The Great Empress*</u> *because it shows a*
royal Chinese woman.

Write your title and explain why you chose it.

_____

_____

COMPARE & CONTRAST

Look at *The Ocean Is the Dragon's World* and *Camas para Sueños* again. Write three details about the woman in *The Ocean Is the Dragon's World*.

Example: *The woman has very long fingernails.*

1. _____

2. _____

3. _____

Write three details about the mother in *Camas para Sueños*.

4. _____

5. _____

6. _____

How are the two figures similar?

_____

_____

How are the two figures different?

_____

_____

Copyright © by Pearson Education, Inc.

What is the human spirit?

READING 1: From *César Chávez: We Can Do It!*

VOCABULARY **Key Words** *Use with textbook page 305.*

Write each word in the box next to its definition.

~~chemicals~~	crops	demand	migrant workers	strike	union

Example: ___*chemicals*___: solids, liquids, or gases used in chemistry

1. _____: people who go to another area or country to find work

2. _____: stop working because of a disagreement about pay or working conditions

3. _____: plants such as corn or wheat that farmers sell

4. _____: an organization of workers that bargains as a group

5. _____: ask strongly for something

Use the words in the box at the top of the page to complete the sentences.

6. Members of the _____ asked for more pay.

7. The workers decided to protest by going on _____.

8. The fields have produced more _____ this summer.

9. _____ move to wherever they can find jobs.

10. The women stopped work to _____ the same pay as men.

Copyright © by Pearson Education, Inc.

Read the paragraph below. Pay attention to the underlined academic words.

> A trade union is a group of workers who bargain together to improve their wages, benefits and working conditions. The idea behind a union is that workers who stand together have a stronger <u>impact</u>. One of the best-known unions is The American Federation of Labor. It was <u>founded</u> in 1886 by Samuel Gompers. Its first aim was to protect the safety of workers who performed manual <u>labor</u>. Gompers' <u>persistence</u> led to better pay, shorter hours and more job security for all union members.

Write the letter of the correct definition next to each word.

Example: ___c___ founded

_____ **1.** labor

_____ **2.** persistence

_____ **3.** impact

a. work that requires a lot of physical effort

b. determination to do something even though it is difficult or other people oppose it

c. established a business, organization, school, etc.

d. effect that an event or situation has on someone or something

Use the academic words from the exercise above to complete the sentences.

4. The school was _____ in 1861, but moved in 1916.

5. The speech had a great _____ on everyone who heard it.

6. Construction workers have a job that requires a lot of hard _____.

7. He didn't know the answer right away, but with his _____, he finally got it.

Complete the sentences with your own ideas.

Example: Students who show great persistence __*often do well in school*__.

8. The last experience that had a great impact on me was

_____.

9. Our town was founded in _____.

10. The last time I did hard labor was _____.

Copyright © by Pearson Education, Inc.

Name _____ Date _____

WORD STUDY **Capitalization** *Use with textbook page 307.*

REMEMBER Capitalize the word *I*, the first letter of the first word in a sentence, all proper nouns, names, and titles of people. Also capitalize geographical terms (and streets, cities, states, countries, continents), historical events (eras, calendar items), and the names of ethnic groups, national groups, and languages.

Look at the chart below. Capitalize each word correctly. Write the correct word in the chart. Then write the rule.

Incorrect Capitalization	Correct Capitalization	Rule
Today i walk the dog.	I	Capitalize I.
1. the moon is full tonight.		
2. My father is dr. lee.		
3. We visit the grand canyon.		
4. Tomorrow is thanksgiving.		
5. Risa studies spanish.		

Look at the sentences below. Write corrected sentences on the lines.

Example: a new chinese restaurant opened on main street.

A new Chinese restaurant opened on Main Street.

6. the red cross, a health group, went to haiti where many people speak french.

_____

7. we study the renaissance and the revolutionary war in mr. smith's class.

_____

8. i live at 22 vine avenue in st. louis, missouri.

_____

9. the empire state building and the statue of liberty are located in new york city.

_____

10. my birthday is on the last monday in may, the same as memorial day.

_____

Copyright © by Pearson Education, Inc.

Unit 5 • **Reading 1** **163**

Use with textbook page 307.

REMEMBER When you read, distinguish fact from opinion. A fact is a statement that can be proven, and can be checked with research. An opinion is a person's point of view about a topic. Writers often state opinions with adjectives and with such words as *I think, I believe, I suppose,* and *personally.*

Read each paragraph. Then answer the questions below.

1. Some boys go to all boy schools. I think those schools are a great idea.

   Which statement above is a fact?

   _____

2. Which statement in #1 is an opinion?

   _____

3. Some dogs weigh only a few pounds, but others are huge. Tiny dogs are the cutest.

   Which statement above is a fact?

   _____

4. Which statement in #3 is an opinion?

   _____

5. How can the strategy of distinguishing fact from opinion help you become a better reader?

   _____

   _____

Copyright © by Pearson Education, Inc.

COMPREHENSION   *Use with textbook page 314.*

Choose the best answer for each item. Circle the letter of the correct answer.

1. César Chávez's family became farm workers _____.

   a. during the Depression   **b.** during the
Roaring Twenties   **c.** when Chávez founded
the NFWA

2. César Chávez saw that _____.

   a. migrant workers received
good wages   **b.** migrant workers were
treated unfairly   **c.** a migrant workers had
good benefits

3. César started the NFWA to _____.

   a. give farm workers a union   **b.** get more publicity   **c.** rejoin the U.S. Navy

4. The 1965 boycott against California grape growers _____.

   a. was successful   **b.** ended in failure   **c.** went unnoticed

5. César's work on behalf of farmers resulted in _____.

   a. further crackdowns   **b.** new laws protecting
workers' rights   **c.** a sharp increase in the
prices of California
grapes

EXTENSION   *Use with textbook page 315.*

César Chávez tried to help migrant workers, whose lives were difficult. Think about farm labor and about moving around a lot. Write a paragraph about why it would be difficult to be a migrant worker.

_____

_____

_____

_____

Copyright © by Pearson Education, Inc.

> **REMEMBER** A phrasal verb is made up of a verb and one or more prepositions. The meaning of a phrasal verb differs from the meaning of the original verb.
> **Example:** I try to work out at the gym every day. *Work* means *to labor*, but the phrasal verb *work out* means *to exercise*.
> When a phrasal verb is inseparable, a noun or pronoun cannot be placed between the verb and the preposition that follows it.
> **Example:** She dropped out of the race.
> Notice that *the race* must follow the phrasal verb *dropped out of*.

Underline the phrasal verb in each sentence below.

Example: My mother <u>works out</u> every day.

1. He got into the backseat of the car.

2. She was not feeling well, and yesterday she came down with a cold.

3. When you are walking, hold on to the handrail so that you do not fall.

4. We went over our tests in class so we could see our mistakes.

5. It was hard to catch up with Cyrus. He ran very fast.

Read the definitions of each phrasal verb in parentheses. Then write a sentence with the phrasal verb. (Some phrasal verbs have more than one meaning. Use the meaning that is given here.)

Example: (wait up for = stay awake until someone arrives)

   Whenever I go out in the evening, my mother waits up for me.

6. (look after = take care of someone)

   _____

7. (come across = find something accidentally or unexpectedly)

   _____

8. (not give in = not stop fighting)

   _____

Copyright © by Pearson Education, Inc.

Separable Phrasal Verbs *Use with textbook page 317.*

> **REMEMBER** When a phrasal verb is separable, the object can either follow the preposition or come between the verb and preposition. When the object is a pronoun, it must come between the verb and preposition.
> **Examples:** Please *bring back* your library book. Please *bring* it *back*.

Circle the best definition for each underlined separable phrasal verb.

Example: She <u>called</u> the wedding <u>off</u>. She was in love with someone else.

    (a.) canceled   **b.** held

1. The teacher <u>gave</u> our tests <u>back</u>.

    a. took   **b.** returned

2. Can I <u>get back</u> my CD? I'd really like to listen to it.

    a. give   **b.** receive

3. Brett has <u>set up</u> a website where you can see his photos.

    a. closed   **b.** arranged

4. She <u>turned off</u> the TV.

    a. started   **b.** stopped

Rewrite the sentences in the exercise above, placing the object either between the preposition and the verb or after the preposition.

Example: _She called off the wedding._____

5. _____

6. _____

7. _____

8. _____

Copyright © by Pearson Education, Inc.

Complete a word web, and use it to write an advertisement for a product of your choice.

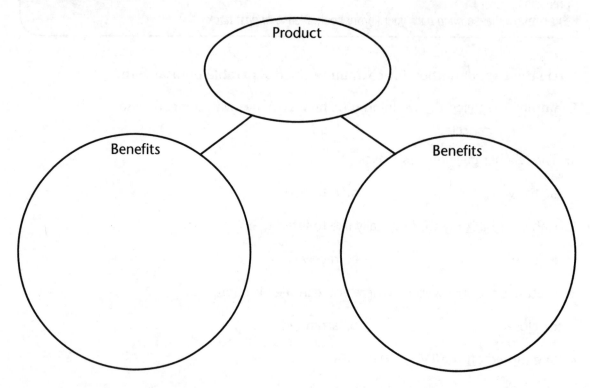

Use the Peer Review Checklist below to obtain feedback from your partner. This feedback will help you edit your final draft.

PEER REVIEW CHECKLIST

☐ Does the paragraph begin with an attention-grabbing phrase or question?

☐ Does the paragraph include facts and details to try and persuade the audience?

☐ Does the paragraph explain the benefits of the product or service?

☐ Are the details interesting and convincing enough to persuade the reader?

☐ Are phrasal verbs used correctly?

☐ What changes could be made to improve the advertisement?

Copyright © by Pearson Education, Inc.

UNIT 5 — What is the human spirit?

READING 2: "The Scholarship Jacket"

VOCABULARY   **Literary Words** *Use with textbook page 321.*

> **REMEMBER** A **dialogue** is a conversation between characters. Dialogue is shown with quotation marks. Quotation marks let you know which character is speaking and how the dialogue should be read. The **theme** is a central message in a story. Usually it is not stated directly. You must decide what the theme is by looking closely at the work.

Read each sentence below. If a sentence contains dialogue, write *yes* in the space provided. If a sentence does not contain dialogue, write *no* in the space provided.

Dialogue?	Sentence
yes	Darrell said, "You should come to dinner with Jen and me."
1.	"I've been listening to this song all day," she said, grinning.
2.	We told them we would show up later in the evening.
3.	It's always been easy for her.
4.	I responded, "I don't think it exists."

Read the dialogue below. Answer the question below.

"How are you doing?" Sarah asked, sitting beside Leah.
"Not great!" Leah replied. "I haven't finished my work and it's so late." She sighed.
Sarah smiled helpfully. "Would you like me to stay up a while with you?" she asked.
Leah beamed back. "Thanks, I really could use some help."
"Excellent!" Sarah said. "I'll make cocoa."

5. What is one theme of the passage above? _____

Copyright © by Pearson Education, Inc.

Read the paragraph below. Pay attention to the underlined academic words.

Our school <u>principal</u> was a member of Hasty Pudding Theatricals. This group is made up of Harvard University students and is the oldest <u>academic</u> theater group in the United States. The name comes from an early <u>policy</u> where members had to bring a pot of hasty pudding to gatherings. One famous Hasty Pudding <u>tradition</u> is that men perform all the roles, both male and female. Women, like our principal, don't perform, but they can direct and work backstage.

Write the academic words from the paragraph above next to their correct definitions.

Example: _____*policy*_____: a plan that is agreed to by a political party, government, or organization

1. _____: someone who is in charge of a school

2. _____: a belief or custom that has existed for a long time

3. _____: relating to work done in schools, colleges, or universities

Use the academic words from the exercise above to complete the sentences.

4. Each new student in our school has a chance to meet the _____.

5. The company changed its _____ to allow longer vacations.

6. The student enjoyed both athletic and _____ success.

7. In some families, it's a _____ to pray before each meal.

Complete the sentences with your own ideas.

Example: The principal of my school is named ___*Mr. Ward*___.

8. The academic subject that I find most challenging is

_____.

9. I find the tradition of _____ interesting.

10. I believe that the government can make things better for citizens by changing its

_____ policy.

Copyright © by Pearson Education, Inc.

WORD STUDY Words Ending with Consonant + *-le, -al, -el*

Use with textbook page 323.

> **REMEMBER** In English, many words end with a consonant and *-le* as in *thimble*, *-al* as in *mental*, or *-el* as in *gavel*. There are no rules for spelling these words, so it's best to memorize the spelling for each.

Read the words in the box below. Then write each word in the correct column in the chart.

tickle	lapel	rental	sample	
corral	dispel	hotel	example	oriental

Consonant + *-le*	Consonant + *-al*	Consonant + *-el*
tickle		

Underline the two-word letter pattern at the end of each word below. Then write a sentence using the word. Use a dictionary if needed.

Example: divisib<u>le</u>   *Four, six, and eight are divisible by two.* _____

1. pickle   _____

2. canal   _____

3. capital   _____

4. novel   _____

5. sentimental   _____

6. camel   _____

7. candle   _____

Copyright © by Pearson Education, Inc.

> **REMEMBER** Drawing inferences helps you figure out information that an author does not give directly. As you read, think about the characters and the setting, as well as your own experiences.

Read each paragraph and answer the questions that follow.

When Libby's dad signed her up for the swim club she was angry. The first day, she could swim only two laps, while kids half her age swam for hours without getting tired. But after the first month, she could swim twenty laps without stopping. When Libby told her dad that the coach wanted her to join a swim meet, he was surprised by her reaction.

1. What can you infer about Libby's reaction from the passage above?

_____

_____

2. What event from your own experience has helped you understand Libby's feelings?

_____

_____

Dan and Evan had been best friends since second grade, even though they were complete opposites. Dan loved sports. He played baseball, soccer, lacrosse, and football. Evan dreamed of being a famous movie director. Then Carlos moved into the house between the two boys. Carlos loved movies just as much as Evan did.

3. What can you infer about how Carlos' arrival may affect the friendship between Dan and Evan?

_____

_____

4. What event or knowledge from your own experience helped you to make an inference about the passage?

_____

_____

5. How do you think drawing inferences can help you to understand what you read better?

_____

_____

Copyright © by Pearson Education, Inc.

COMPREHENSION *Use with textbook page 332.*

Choose the best answer for each item. Circle the letter of the correct answer.

1. Each year in Marta's school a scholarship jacket was awarded to _____.

   a. the best athlete in the school

   b. the student who had the highest grades for eight years

   c. the child of a school board member

2. The board was going to give the jacket to Joann because _____.

   a. she had the highest grades

   b. Marta didn't want it

   c. her father was important in the town

3. The board changed its policy about the jacket being free to _____.

   a. have a reason to award it to Joann

   b. raise some extra money

   c. help Marta understand what it was worth

4. Marta's grandfather refused to pay for the jacket because _____.

   a. Marta had earned it

   b. it was too expensive

   c. he was busy with his work

5. In the end the principal decided to _____.

   a. ignore the whole situation

   b. award the jacket to Joann because she could pay for it

   c. do the right thing and award it to Marta

RESPONSE to LITERATURE *Use with textbook page 333.*

Imagine the graduation ceremony that takes place after the events in "The Scholarship Jacket." Is Grandfather there? Are the teachers there? How is Marta dressed? How does she feel? Draw a picture of the scene in the space below.

Copyright © by Pearson Education, Inc.

> **REMEMBER** Place quotation marks (" ") around direct speech (what someone says) and capitalize the first word of direct speech. Use a comma to separate direct speech from the phrase that identifies the speaker.
> **Example:** She said, "You did a good job."
> When the direct speech ends with a question mark (**?**) or an exclamation point (**!**), use that mark instead of the comma.
> **Example:** "What a great job you did!" she exclaimed.
> When the phrase that identifies the speaker comes in the middle of direct speech, use one comma after the first part of the speech and another comma after the phrase.
> **Example:** "You did a good job," she said, "and I'm proud of you."

Put a ✓ next to the sentence in each pair that is correctly punctuated.

_____ 1. The teacher said, "You have made good progress."

_____ The teacher said, You have made good progress.

_____ 2. "Run with the ball" the coach exclaimed.

_____ "Run with the ball!" the coach exclaimed.

_____ 3. "Who won the scholarship," asked the principal.

_____ "Who won the scholarship?" asked the principal.

_____ 4. "Write your name on every page" said the teacher.

_____ "Write your name on every page," said the teacher.

_____ 5. "Study hard," she said, "and you will surely do well."

_____ "Study hard," she said, and you will surely do well."

Fix each of the sentences below by adding correct punctuation.

6. My name is Maria she said

7. He said Tomorrow is my birthday

8. What is your name she asked

9. What a good idea he exclaimed

10. I'm having a party she said and I'd like you to come

Copyright © by Pearson Education, Inc.

Reported Speech: Reporting Verbs *said, asked, told*

Use with textbook page 335.

> **REMEMBER** Use the reporting verb *said* (*that*) when reporting statements.
> **Example:** She *said* (*that*) she would come.
> Use the reporting verb *asked* when reporting questions. Sometimes an object follows *asked*, but not always. Use statement, not question, word order.
> **Examples:** He *asked* (*me*) *where* I was going. (*Wh-* question + subject + verb)
> He *asked* (*me*) *if* I was going. (*Yes-No* question + *if* or *whether* + subject + verb)
> Use the reporting verb *told* when you mention who is being spoken to. An object always follows *told*, which is often followed by *that*.
> **Example:** She *told me* (*that*) she would come.

Complete each sentence with the correct reporting verb: *said, asked,* **or** *told.*

Example: He _____*asked*_____ her if she would go to the dance.

1. They _____ me that they were on their way.

2. Theo _____ he was working this Friday.

3. I _____ Dominic that he could come with us.

4. Carter _____ me if he could borrow my car.

5. Steve _____ whether he could help.

6. Angie _____ that she would bring chips to the party.

7. Myra _____ Nick that she wasn't coming.

8. Fred _____ that I was right.

Copyright © by Pearson Education, Inc.

Complete your own idea web for a review of a book, CD, play, or film.

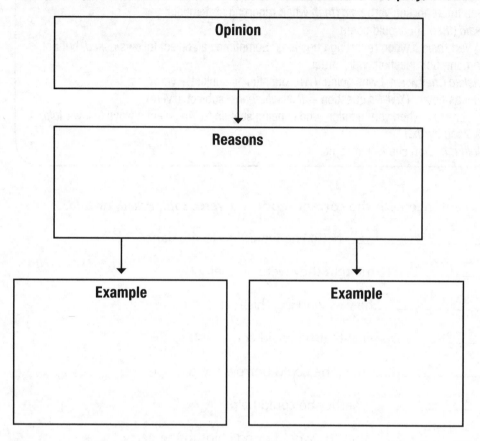

Use the Peer Review Checklist below to obtain feedback from your partner. This feedback will help you edit your final draft.

PEER REVIEW CHECKLIST

☐ Does the paragraph include the main points of the film or book?

☐ Is the writer's opinion clearly stated?

☐ Is the writer's opinion supported with details and examples?

☐ Is punctuation used correctly?

☐ Is reported speech used correctly?

☐ What changes could be made to improve the paragraph?

Copyright © by Pearson Education, Inc.

UNIT 5

What is the human spirit?

READING 3: From *The Diary of Anne Frank: The Play*

VOCABULARY **Literary Words** *Use with textbook page 339.*

> **REMEMBER** A **drama** is a play that is performed by actors. It consists of dialogue and **stage directions**. Stage directions describe the action and environment onstage. They are often printed in italics or brackets. A **diary** is a book in which you write about your own life and thoughts.

Read each sentence in the chart. Imagine that you are reading the diary of someone your age. Write *diary* if you think the sentence comes from a diary. Write *fiction* if you think the sentence is from a work of fiction.

Diary or Work of Fiction?	Description
fiction	Paula held the jewel up to the light.
1.	The earth is hollow inside.
2.	We spent the day playing at the park, and I had a great time.
3.	I think Andrea is feeling better this week.

Read the following excerpt from a play.

> DON: [*angrily*] Give it back, Rob! I'm warning you.
>
> ROB: Don, you know I didn't take Cathy's letter. [*Sighing*] I would never do that.
>
> [*Rob reaches out a hand to Don, who refuses to take it.*]
>
> DON: Well if you didn't take it, who did? The cat?
>
> [*Rob's cat walks across the stage in a purple spotlight. They watch it go.*]
>
> ROB: Somehow I doubt it, Donnie.
>
> [*After a moment they both smile.*]

4. **Underline the names of the speakers, and circle the stage directions.**

5. **Write two more lines of dialogue for the scene between Don and Rob.**

_____

_____

Copyright © by Pearson Education, Inc.

Read the paragraph below. Pay attention to the underlined academic words.

> Our school has <u>published</u> a student handbook for new students. The handbook has information about the school and lists <u>regulations</u> that students must obey. It also lists rules about how to behave when entering and leaving school. For example, we are not supposed to make noise in front of the school, as this would disturb the <u>occupants</u> of the apartment building next door. Though the handbook contains a lot of information, it has <u>assisted</u> many new students in adjusting to our school.

Write the academic words from the paragraph above next to their correct definitions.

Example: _regulations_ : official rules or orders

1. _____: helped someone

2. _____: printed and distributed

3. _____: people who live in a building, room, etc.

Use the academic words from the exercise above to complete the sentences.

4. Her new book is going to be _____ next month.

5. The tutor _____ me with my homework.

6. The _____ of the apartment weren't home when we visited.

7. In the lab, it's important to follow safety _____ so you don't get hurt.

Complete the sentences with your own ideas.

Example: The older students have assisted the _incoming freshman_ .

8. If I ever write a book that is published, it will probably be about

    _____.

9. The occupants of my home are _____.

10. In my school there are important regulations to follow, such as

    _____.

Copyright © by Pearson Education, Inc.

WORD STUDY Spelling the Sound /j/ *Use with textbook page 341.*

REMEMBER The sound /j/ can be spelled *j* as in *jam*, *g* as in *gentle*, or *dge* as in *ledge*. The letter *j* is usually used before *a, o,* or *u*. The letter *g* is usually used before *e, i,* or *y*. The letters *dge* are often used when the sound comes at the end of a syllable or word. Knowing these patterns can help you spell and pronounce the words correctly.

Read the words in the box below. Then write each word in the correct column in the chart.

project	lodge	general	acknowledge	jacket
wedge	Japan	giraffe	gym	

/j/ spelled *j*	/j/ spelled *g*	/j/ spelled *dge*
project		

Write the pattern for /j/ in each word below.

Example: bridge ___*/j/ spelled dge*___

1. genuine _____

2. reject _____

3. energy _____

4. pledge _____

5. January _____

6. giant _____

7. journal _____

Copyright © by Pearson Education, Inc.

> **REMEMBER** Learning to read aloud brings a story and characters to life.

Read each passage. Then answer the questions.

Lucy: Remember when we had that big fight?
Jenna: I'm sorry about that. I didn't mean those things I said.
Lucy: I forgive you, because it's important to forgive your friends, right?
Jenna: Right!
Lucy: Then I hope you'll forgive me, because I just crashed your bike.

1. If you were reading Jenna's first line, what emotion would you show?

   _____

   _____

2. If you were reading Lucy's last line, what emotion would you show?

   _____

   _____

Dad: You can't go to the party and that's final.
Raymond: But you said I could go!
Dad: That's before I found out that the party is 100 miles away!
Raymond: That's so unfair!

3. If you were reading Dad's lines, what emotion would be in your voice?

   _____

4. How does the punctuation in this passage help you to know how to read Raymond's lines?

   _____

   _____

5. How do you think the strategy of reading aloud with expression will make you a better reader?

   _____

   _____

Copyright © by Pearson Education, Inc.

COMPREHENSION *Use with textbook page 350.*

Choose the best answer for each item. Circle the letter of the correct answer.

1. The Franks moved into the Secret Annex when _____.

   a. the Germans invaded Holland and the Dutch surrendered
   b. Anne's sister was ordered to work in Germany
   c. Anne turned sixteen

2. The Franks were hidden by _____.

   a. two former work colleagues
   b. Peter van Daan and his family
   c. the secret police

3. When Peter arrives, Anne feels quite _____.

   a. worried
   b. protective of her space
   c. excited

4. While Anne is positive and upbeat, the adults are _____.

   a. nervous
   b. arguing
   c. bored

5. Reading a play rather than a diary allows you to experience _____.

   a. a nonfiction account
   b. one person's voice
   c. many points of view

RESPONSE TO LITERATURE *Use with textbook page 351.*

Anne Frank hid in a tiny annex with her family for two years. They couldn't walk the streets or make too much noise, and lived on very little food. They lived in fear of capture. Try to imagine living in those conditions. In the space below, write a short paragraph describing how that might feel.

_____

_____

_____

_____

_____

Copyright © by Pearson Education, Inc.

REMEMBER The present perfect is formed with *have* or *has* + the past participle of a verb. It describes an action that began in the past and continues into the present.
When *for* is used with the present perfect, it specifies the exact point in time when an activity began.
Example: She *has played* the piano *for two years*.
When *since* is used with the present perfect, it specifies the exact point in time when an activity began.
Example: She *has practiced* this composition *since January*.
Use adverbs such as *just*, *yet*, *already*, *ever*, *before*, and *never* to show different time orders.
Example: Have you ever seen a full moon? No, I never have.

Circle the correct adverb to complete each sentence.

Example: Our school has (just / before) hired a new soccer coach.

1. Our local soccer team has (never / ever) played well.

2. The team has (before / already) won the championship game.

3. Have you been to the aquarium (before / just)?

4. She's (yet / already) finished her test.

5. I haven't seen that movie (already / yet).

Answer each question with information about yourself, using the present perfect and *for* or *since*.

Example: How long have you lived here? *I've lived here since I was three.*

6. How long have you lived here? _____

7. How long have you studied English? _____

8. How long have you known your best friend? _____

Copyright © by Pearson Education, Inc.

Present Perfect Progressive *Use with textbook page 353.*

REMEMBER Use the present perfect progressive to emphasize the duration of an action that was in progress in the past and may continue into the present. *For, since,* and the phrases *all morning, all day long,* etc., signal the present perfect progressive. Form the present perfect progressive with *has* or *have* + *been* + the present participle.
Example: He *has been studying* all morning. (He is still studying *or* he has just finished.)

Complete the sentences with the present perfect progressive form of the verb in parentheses. Then write whether the action *continues* or is *completed*.

Example: He __*has been working*_____ (work) in this company since 1999.

_____*continues*_____

1. I _____ (wait) for you since two o'clock. What took you

   so long? _____

2. Marta _____ (live) in Kiev since 2001.

   _____

3. He's tired because he _____ (play) handball for two

   hours. _____

4. We _____ (look) for the exit for an hour and still

   haven't found it. _____

5. How long _____ she _____

   (work) in the garden? It's getting hot. _____

6. It _____ (snow) for hours and is still coming down.

   _____

7. They _____ (talk) for the last hour. _____

8. What _____ you _____

   (do) for the last 20 minutes? _____

9. Jim _____ (teach) at the school for the last three years.

   _____

10. I _____ (exercise) a lot lately. _____

Copyright © by Pearson Education, Inc.

Use with textbook pages 354–355.

Complete your own pros-and-cons chart for a paragraph on an issue you feel strongly about.

Pros	Cons

Use the Peer Review Checklist below to obtain feedback from your partner. This feedback will help you edit your final draft.

PEER REVIEW CHECKLIST

☐ Is the main issue clearly presented?

☐ Is the writer's opinion clearly stated?

☐ Does the writer give supporting reasons for this opinion?

☐ Are both sides of the argument presented?

☐ Does the writer give reasons for disagreeing with the opposing arguments?

☐ Are present perfect and present perfect progressive used correctly?

☐ What changes could be made to improve the paragraph?

Copyright © by Pearson Education, Inc.

Name _____ Date _____

What is the human spirit?

READING 4: "Listen Up"

VOCABULARY **Key Words** *Use with textbook page 357.*

Write each word in the box next to its definition.

| accomplish | communicate | hearing impaired | obstacle | opponent | sign language |

Example: _____*obstacle*_____: something that makes it difficult for you to succeed

1. _____: succeed in doing something

2. _____: a language for the deaf, using hand movements instead of spoken words

3. _____: exchange information or conversation with other people

4. _____: someone who tries to defeat another person or team in a competition

5. _____: unable to hear well or at all

Use the words in the box at the top of the page to complete the sentences.

6. The deaf woman was able to converse using _____.

7. The young tennis player was nervous about meeting his _____.

8. Will you be able to _____ your goal this week?

9. Some good friends can _____ without saying a word.

10. The biggest _____ to living in Antarctica is staying warm.

Copyright © by Pearson Education, Inc.

Read the paragraph below. Pay attention to the underlined academic words.

Brainstorming is when a <u>team</u> of people work together to come up with ideas and solve problems. <u>Prior</u> to the 1930s, there was no name for this method. Then advertising executive Alex Faickney Osborn coined the phrase "brainstorming." He could <u>perceive</u> brainstorming to be a very effective problem-solving technique. He felt that the more workers he got to <u>participate</u> in a brainstorming session, the quicker a problem would be solved.

Write the letter of the correct definition next to each word.

Example: ___c___ perceive

_____ **1.** team

_____ **2.** prior

_____ **3.** participate

a. before

b. take part in an activity or event

c. understand or think about something in a particular way

d. a group of people who compete against another group in a sport, game, etc.

Use the academic words from the exercise above to complete the sentences.

4. The coach recruited five new players for her _____.

5. Mayor Burrell invited every citizen to _____ in the festival.

6. Three people can _____ the same event in three different ways.

7. _____ to 1973, my family lived in Arizona.

Complete the sentences with your own ideas.

Example: ___My grandfather_____ has told me many stories about prior generations.

8. A team I would like to join is _____.

9. I like to participate in _____.

10. It's sometimes difficult to perceive the problems of _____.

Copyright © by Pearson Education, Inc.

WORD STUDY Antonyms *Use with textbook page 359.*

REMEMBER Antonyms are words that have opposite or nearly opposite meanings. For example, *near* is an antonym for *far*. Learning antonyms helps you express your exact meaning and figure out the meaning of words you do not know.

Look at the chart below. Write an antonym for each word. Use a thesaurus or a dictionary if needed.

Words	Antonym
ending	*beginning*
1. friend	
2. distant	
3. optimistic	
4. defeat	
5. agitated	

Look at the chart below. Write an antonym for each word. Then write a sentence using the antonym. Use a thesaurus or a dictionary if needed.

Word	Antonym	Sentence
courageous	*cowardly*	*The cowardly lion ran from the mouse.*
6. expensive		
7. early		
8. succeed		
9. generous		
10. enormous		

Copyright © by Pearson Education, Inc.

> **REMEMBER** When you read, identify the main idea and details. The main idea is the most important idea in a text. The details are small pieces of information that support the main idea.

Read each paragraph. Then answer the questions that follow.

1. Washing your hands is good for your health. Many germs are spread through human contact. When you shake hands with someone, touch a doorknob, or borrow a pen, you can get germs on your hands. If you then touch your mouth or eyes, you spread the germs. Scrubbing with soap and water can take away the harmful germs.

   What is the main idea of the passage above?

   _____

   _____

2. What are the details that support the main idea?

   _____

   _____

3. Pasta is easy to make and fun to eat. Did you know that you can make it yourself? All it takes is flour, eggs and a pinch of salt. You take these ingredients and work them into a dough with your hands. Then you roll them out with a rolling pin. You can cut the dough into any shape you want. After you let it dry for a little while, you can cook it just like pasta from a box, except not quite as long. Look for a recipe and try it out!

   What is the main idea of the passage above?

   _____

   _____

4. What are the details that support the main idea?

   _____

   _____

5. How can identifying the main idea and details help you read with greater comprehension?

   _____

Copyright © by Pearson Education, Inc.

Name _____ Date _____

COMPREHENSION   *Use with textbook page 364.*

Choose the best answer for each item. Circle the letter of the correct answer.

1. The CSDR Cubs play against _____.

   a. only hearing-impaired schools   **b.** only hearing schools   **c.** both hearing and hearing-impaired schools

2. Before Coach Gonzales came, the team _____.

   a. had low morale and often lost   **b.** had high morale and often won   **c.** didn't even play games

3. In 2004, the CSDR team had a _____.

   a. losing record   **b.** winning record   **c.** tied record

4. The players communicate with _____.

   a. a spoken code   **b.** hand signals   **c.** coded messages to the cheerleaders

5. To congratulate the players, the fans _____.

   a. yell and scream   **b.** stamp their feet   **c.** raise their arms and wiggle their fingers

EXTENSION   *Use with textbook page 365.*

Pick five words or phrases and write them below. Then research how to express them in American Sign Language. Write a description of the ASL gesture in the right-hand column. Then practice the Sign Language gesture with a classmate. Can you form a simple sentence using only your hands?

English	Description of ASL Gesture
applause	*arms straight up in air, wiggle fingers*

Unit 5 • Reading 4

REMEMBER The present perfect is formed with *have* or *has* + the past participle of a verb. It describes an action that began in the past and continues into the present.

When *for* is used with the present perfect, it describes a period of time that began in the past.

Example: She has played the piano for two years.

When *since* is used with the present perfect, it specifies the exact point in time when an activity began.

Example: She *has practiced* this composition *since January*.

Use adverbs such as *always, often, ever, never,* and *recently* to talk about when or how often something happened in the past.

Example: Have you ever seen a full moon? No, I never have.

Circle the correct adverb to complete each sentence.

Example: Our school has ((recently)/so far) hired a new soccer coach.

1. Our local soccer team has (always/ever) played well.

2. The team has (often/so far) won the championship game.

Answer each question below, using the present perfect with *for* or *since*.

Example: How long has he played football? (for)

   He has played football for two seasons.

3. How long has she taken dance lessons? (since)

   _____

4. How long have they planned the party? (for)

   _____

5. How long has he dreamed of attending college? (since)

   _____

Copyright © by Pearson Education, Inc.

Past Perfect *Use with textbook page 367.*

> **REMEMBER** Use the past perfect to tell about events that happened at an unspecified time in the past. When the simple past is used with the past perfect, the clause in the past perfect tells about the first event; the clause in the simple past tells about the second. Form the past perfect with *had* + the past participle. Use *hadn't* to form the negative and begin questions with *had*.
> **Example:** I *hadn't been* there long when Sidney *walked* in.

Underline the clause in each sentence that shows the first action.

Example: My brother ate all the cake <u>that our mom had made</u>.

1. When she went out to play, she had already done her homework.

2. I could not remember the poem we had learned.

3. The children collected the apples that had fallen from the tree.

4. Had he phoned Mitzi before he went to see her in London?

Complete each sentence with the past perfect or the simple past form of the verbs in parentheses.

Example: The storm ___*destroyed*___ (destroy) the sand castle we ___*had made*___ (make).

5. The doctor _____ (take off) the cast that he _____ (put on) in August.

6. Christine _____ (not ride) a horse before that day.

7. I _____ (study) Lithuanian for five years before I

   _____ (speak) it fluently.

8. He _____ (not be) to Washington until last month.

Copyright © by Pearson Education, Inc.

Complete your own word web about an issue you feel strongly about in your school or community.

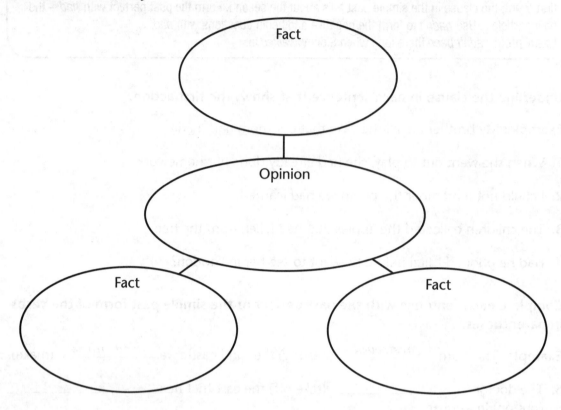

Use the Peer Review Checklist below to obtain feedback from your partner. This feedback will help you edit your final draft.

PEER REVIEW CHECKLIST

☐ Does the first sentence explain the main issue?

☐ Is the writer's opinion clearly stated?

☐ Does the writer support each statement with facts or examples?

☐ Does the writer clearly state what kind of action needs to be taken?

☐ Are past perfect and past perfect progressive used correctly?

☐ What changes could be made to improve the letter?

Copyright © by Pearson Education, Inc.

WRITING WORKSHOP   *Use with textbook pages 374–378.*

Organize your ideas in the graphic organizer below.

Pros	Cons

Use the Peer Review Checklist below to obtain feedback from your partner. This feedback will help you edit your final draft.

PEER REVIEW CHECKLIST

☐ Was the writer's opinion clearly presented?

☐ Was the opinion supported with details and facts?

☐ Did the writer present both sides of the argument?

☐ Did the writer give reasons for not agreeing with the opposing position?

☐ Did the concluding paragraph sum up the main points in a memorable way?

☐ What changes could be made to improve the essay?

Copyright © by Pearson Education, Inc.

Underline the vocabulary items you know and can use well. Review and practice any you haven't underlined. Underline them when you know them well.

Literary Words	Key Words	Academic Words	
dialogue	chemicals	founded	assisted
theme	crops	impact	occupants
diary	demand	labor	published
drama	migrant workers	persistence	regulations
stage directions	strike	academic	participate
	union	policy	perceive
	appearance	principal	prior
	autobiography	tradition	team
	orphanage		
	persistent		
	sharecroppers		
	slight		

Put a check by the skills you can perform well. Review and practice any you haven't checked off. Check them off when you can perform them well.

Skills	I can . . .
Word Study	☐ recognize and spell capitalized words. ☐ recognize and spell words ending with consonant + *-le, -al,* and *-el.* ☐ recognize and spell words with the /j/ sound. ☐ recognize antonyms.
Reading Strategies	☐ distinguish fact from opinion. ☐ draw inferences. ☐ read aloud. ☐ identify the main idea and details.
Grammar	☐ use inseparable and separable phrasal verbs. ☐ use punctuation in quotations and use reporting verbs *said, asked, told.* ☐ use the present perfect and present perfect progressive. ☐ use the past perfect and past perfect progressive.
Writing	☐ write an advertisement. ☐ write a review of a book, film, or play. ☐ write a persuasive paragraph. ☐ write a letter to the editor. ☐ write a persuasive speech.

Copyright © by Pearson Education, Inc.

Copyright © by Pearson Education, Inc.

TEST 1

DIRECTIONS
Read this selection. Then choose the best word to complete the sentences.

History Report

Today students are reading about what they will need to do to complete a report for a history class. The selection below is about preparing to present the report.

1   After you have finished your research, you are ready to create note cards. You will use the note cards to remind you of the information you found. This lets you talk about your ___1___, instead of reading the entire report. This makes your presentation more interesting to listen to.

2   The note cards should each give an important fact about this ___2___ in history. Add details about the fact on the card. Do not write in complete sentences. Just write phrases that will remind you of what to say.

3   After you write all of your note cards, put them in order. You can group your cards by ___3___ ideas, or you can put them in time order. Make sure that the grouping of the ideas will make sense to your audience.

4   Practice giving your report more than once. You should speak for five minutes. If you cannot speak that long, you need more information in your report. If you do not know what to say about a fact, add more details to your note cards. Ask friends or adults to listen to your presentation. Then let them tell you if anything was ___4___.

1 A person
   B project
   C present
   D public

3 A similar
   B interesting
   C faithful
   D concerned

2 F group
   G alarm
   H watch
   J period

4 F undone
   G unclear
   H unopened
   J untied

DIRECTIONS
Read this selection. Then answer the questions that follow it.

The Photographs of Dorothea Lange

1   Dorothea Lange's photographs help us see the world she saw. Lange photographed the world of everyday people with compassion and dedication. She showed how these people dealt with the problems they faced. Her <u>depiction</u> of ordinary people in difficult times has helped us understand our nation's history.

2   She is especially known for her work during the Great Depression. She captured on film families escaping from Dust Bowl farms and migrating west in search of work. Her best-known picture, titled "Migrant Mother," shows a woman who kept her family alive on frozen vegetables taken from the field and birds captured by her children.

3   During World War II, Lange's work showed the effects of the war on the home front. She photographed the internment camps where Japanese Americans were relocated and held during the war. She showed workers, including women and minorities, at California shipyards.

4   Thanks to Lange's photographs, we can see today what she saw years ago; we can look directly at the human spirit of the past. More importantly, her vision helps us see our present-day world more clearly. As Lange said, "The camera is an instrument that teaches people how to see without a camera."

---

1 In paragraph 1, what words help the reader know what *depiction* means?

　A　she showed
　B　the problems
　C　faced
　D　compassion

2 Which sentence is an opinion?

　F　*She photographed the internment camps where Japanese Americans were relocated and held during the war.*
　G　*During World War II, Lange's work showed the effects of the war on the home front.*
　H　*More importantly, her vision helps us see our present-day world more clearly.*
　J　*She captured on film families escaping from Dust Bowl farms and migrating west in search of work.*

3 According to the article, what was one effect of World War II?

　A　Farmers migrating west
　B　People searching for work
　C　Japanese internment camps
　D　Migrating mothers

4 The article suggests that because of Lange's photographs —

　F　people can appreciate how hard life is today
　G　people today can understand how people of the past survived difficulties
　H　people should use a camera in order to understand the past
　J　photographers will continue to take pictures of events in history

Copyright © by Pearson Education, Inc.

TEST 3

DIRECTIONS
Read this selection. Then answer the questions that follow it.

Roberto Clemente

1   Roberto Clemente was born in Puerto Rico in 1934. He was the youngest of seven children. As a child, Roberto loved playing baseball. Because his family didn't have much money, he used tree branches for bats. To make baseballs, he wrapped old golf balls in string and tape.

2   While in high school, Clemente began playing for a professional baseball team in Puerto Rico. Soon, the Los Angeles Dodgers spotted him and hired him to play for a minor league team. One year later, the Pittsburgh Pirates asked him to play for the major leagues. He played right field for the Pirates for eighteen years. During that time he won twelve Golden Glove awards and was voted Most Valuable Player.

3   Though Clemente spoke English, it was not perfect, and sports writers sometimes made fun of him. However, he was proud of his <u>heritage</u>. He did not let the sports writers make him feel ashamed of his traditions and history. He was also determined to help other native Spanish speakers. He helped many young Spanish-speaking baseball players and held baseball clinics for children in Puerto Rico.

4   In 1972, three strong earthquakes hit Nicaragua, killing thousands of people and leaving many homeless. Clemente and four others decided to help the victims by flying a plane to Nicaragua filled with medicine and supplies. His wife begged him not to go because she thought the trip was too dangerous. Unfortunately, she was right. The plane crashed into the ocean, killing all those on board.

5   After his death, Clemente became the first native Spanish speaker to be elected to the Baseball Hall of Fame. Though he died young, he gave a lot to the world during his lifetime.

Copyright © by Pearson Education, Inc.

1 How did Roberto Clemente help other native Spanish speakers?

   A   He flew to Nicaragua to help victims of an earthquake.

   B   He won the Golden Glove Award.

   C   He was voted Most Valuable Player.

   D   He held baseball clinics for children in Puerto Rico.

2 Paragraph 4 is mainly about —

   F   how Roberto Clemente died

   G   how Roberto Clemente helped native Spanish speakers

   H   Roberto Clemente's wife

   J   an earthquake in Nicaragua

3 In paragraph 3, what words help the reader know what *heritage* means?

   A   for children

   B   traditions and history

   C   not perfect

   D   feel ashamed

4 The reader can conclude that Roberto Clemente —

   F   was a good baseball coach

   G   was a talented baseball player

   H   loved his wife and family

   J   was stubborn

5 Which sentence in paragraph 4 shows that Roberto Clemente was kind?

   A   *His wife begged him not to go because she thought the trip was too dangerous.*

   B   *Unfortunately, she was right. The plane crashed into the ocean, killing all those on board.*

   C   *In 1972, three strong earthquakes hit Nicaragua, killing thousands and leaving many homeless.*

   D   *Roberto and four others decided to help the victims by flying a plane to Nicaragua filled with medicine and supplies.*

Visual Literacy: Smithsonian American
Art Museum *Use with textbook pages 380–381.*

LEARNING TO LOOK

**Look at *Spirit of Life* by Daniel Chester French on page 381 in your textbook.
Describe six things you see in this sculpture. State facts, not opinions.**

Example: ___*The figure has wings.*_____

1. _____

2. _____

3. _____

4. _____

5. _____

6. _____

INTERPRETATION

**Look at *Fan Quilt, Mt. Carmel* by the Residents of Bourbon County, Kentucky, on
page 380 in your textbook. Imagine that you are helping them to make the quilt.
Recreate a conversation they might have had. Include yourself as a character!**

Example: ___*This is so time consuming, but I love to sew with different colors.*___

_____

_____

_____

_____

_____

_____

_____

Copyright © by Pearson Education, Inc.

KWLH

Look at *Speaking to Hear* by Michael Olszewski on page 381 in your textbook. Use that artwork to complete the KWLH Chart below.

K	W	L	H
What do you **know** about using fabric in art?	What do you **want** to learn about this work of art?	What have you **learned** about using fabric in art from looking at this work?	**How** have you learned about fabric in art?

Copyright © by Pearson Education, Inc.

How does the sky influence us?

READING 1: "Starry Nights" / "Stars" / "Escape at Bedtime"

VOCABULARY **Literary Words** *Use with textbook page 385.*

> **REMEMBER** A **stanza** is a group of lines in a poem, usually similar in length and pattern. Stanzas are separated by spaces. **Rhyme** is the repetition of sounds at the ends of words. The lines in a stanza sometimes rhyme.

Read each pair of lines. Write *yes* if the lines rhyme. Write *no* if the lines do not rhyme. (Words with similar spellings may not have the same sound.)

Rhyme?	Lines
yes	The snow is very nice But I detest the ice
1.	Lush as a peach, twice as smooth
2.	The passing of time is quick and sublime
3.	Her love was a lamp Illuminating my heart
4.	Alone, in despair He sat in his chair

5. Write a stanza of a poem that has four rhyming lines.

_____

_____

_____

_____

Read the paragraph below. Pay attention to the underlined academic words.

Jackson Pollock was a famous painter. He didn't paint realistic <u>images</u> of people, places, or things. He created paintings by pouring and dripping paint all over a canvas placed on the floor. Each drip and splash is a <u>visible</u> record of how he created the picture. Many art lovers and critics have tried to <u>analyze</u> the meaning behind Pollock's work. One <u>interpretation</u> is that it represents the artist's need to let go and create freely.

Write the letter of the correct definition next to each word.

Example: __*c*__ analyze

_____ **1.** interpretation

_____ **2.** visible

_____ **3.** image

a. something that can be seen

b. a picture that you can see through a camera, on a television, in a mirror, etc.

c. examine or think about something carefully in order to understand it

d. an explanation of the meaning or significance of something

Use the academic words from the exercise above to complete the sentences.

4. The _____ on the movie screen was twenty feet high.

5. Each witness gave a different _____ of what he had heard.

6. We had terrible seats, and the stage was barely _____ from that part of the theater.

7. The scientists took three months to _____ the data from the satellite.

Complete the sentences with your own ideas.

Example: His stories analyze the way people __*show their love*__.

8. I'll always remember the image of _____.

9. What is your interpretation of _____?

10. The _____ is visible from my home.

WORD STUDY Lexical Sets *Use with textbook page 387.*

REMEMBER Words that describe one main idea are called *lexical sets*. For instance, the lexical set for *easy* can include *simple, effortless, straightforward,* and *uncomplicated.* Knowing lexical sets can help you use the precise word you need to convey your meaning.

Look at the chart below. Underline the word that is <u>not</u> part of the lexical set. Use a dictionary if needed.

Word	Word	Word	Word
common	familiar	usual	<u>exotic</u>
1. casual	formal	mellow	easygoing
2. surprising	startling	unanticipated	predictable
3. clean	spotless	tidy	grimy
4. sour	tart	sugary	bitter
5. interesting	dull	appealing	fascinating

Write two or more words for each lexical set. Use a dictionary or thesaurus if needed.

Example: difficult *hard, tough* _____

   6. exciting _____

   7. unusual _____

   8. cheap _____

   9. nice _____

   10. boring _____

Copyright © by Pearson Education, Inc.

Use with textbook page 387.

REMEMBER Analyzing text structure can help you understand what kind of text you're reading. It can also help you set a purpose for reading. Remember that poems have a special text structure. They are arranged in lines and groups of lines called stanzas. Punctuation doesn't always follow the same rules in poetry as it does in other types of text.

Read the poems by Christina Rossetti. Then answer the questions.

53

If stars dropped out of heaven,
And if flowers took their place,
The sky would still look very fair,
And fair earth's face.

Winged angels might fly down to us
To pluck the stars,
But we would only long for flowers
Beyond the cloudy bars.

55

What do the stars do
Up in the sky,
Higher than the winds can blow,
Or the clouds can fly?

Each star in its own glory
Circles, circles still;
As it was lit to shine and set,
And do its Maker's will.

1. What is usually the purpose of reading poems? _____

_____

2. Are there any rhyming lines in either poem? If so, what are they? _____

_____

3. How are the poems similar? _____

_____

4. What different perspectives about stars do the poems give you? _____

_____

5. How can the strategy of analyzing text structure help you become a better reader?

_____

Copyright © by Pearson Education, Inc.

COMPREHENSION   *Use with textbook page 392.*

Choose the best answer for each item. Circle the letter of the correct answer.

1. Van Gogh felt that most paintings of nighttime scenes did not capture night's _____.

   a. loudness   **b.** darkness   **c.** colors

2. Unlike many other painters who worked on nighttime scenes, van Gogh _____.

   a. painted at night   **b.** used mainly   **c.** painted in daylight
                               black paint

3. In the poem "Stars," Sara Teasdale describes the stars as _____.

   a. friendly and close   **b.** angry and fearsome   **c.** distant and amazing

4. The final stanza of Teasdale's poem focuses on _____.

   a. an early morning sky   **b.** a city cafe at night   **c.** the way stars make
                                                                her feel

5. In "Escape at Bedtime," Stevenson rhymes every _____.

   a. two lines   **b.** three lines   **c.** four lines

RESPONSE to LITERATURE   *Use with textbook page 393.*

Van Gogh's description of a café at night is found on page 389 of your textbook. Read his description again. Then draw your own interpretation of what van Gogh saw there.

REMEMBER You can use a semicolon instead of a period to connect two independent clauses that are closely related. A conjunctive adverb or transition often begins the clause after a semicolon.
Example: He wanted to go; however, he didn't have the time.
You can sometimes replace a coordinating conjunction with a semicolon.
Example: Jane was hurt, and she was angry, too. Jane was hurt; she was angry, too.
If groups of items in lists contain commas, semicolons may be used to separate them.
Example: I get my butter, milk, and cheese from Ray's; my vegetables and fruit from the farmer's market; and my meat, fish, and eggs from a local farm.

Add semicolons to the sentences below.

Example: You can have soup or salad to start; ham, beef, or fish for the main course; cake or fruit for dessert; and coffee, tea, or water to drink.

1. I am going home I intend to stay there.

2. It rained all afternoon we managed to have our picnic anyway.

3. She couldn't make it to my party therefore, she brought me flowers the next day.

4. I have been to California, Washington, and Oregon on the West coast Texas and New Mexico in the South and New York, Maine, and Massachusetts in the North.

5. We're going to the concert then we're going out to dinner.

6. Some colleges offer full scholarships others do not.

7. It's such a beautiful day I'll walk to the store.

8. She had very high grades in high school as a result, she got into a good university.

Copyright © by Pearson Education, Inc.

Punctuation: Colons *Use with textbook page 395.*

> **REMEMBER** A colon is often used to introduce a list. The clause before the colon is always an independent clause.
> **Example:** To make clam chowder you need five ingredients: clams, milk, potatoes, butter, and onions.
> NOT To make clam chowder you need: clams, milk, potatoes, butter, and onions.
> A colon can be used when an appositive, or an explanation, is introduced. The appositive may be a word, phrase, or clause.
> **Example:** He was watching his favorite movie: *The Lord of the Rings*.

Draw a line to connect each independent clause on the left with a phrase or clause on the right. Then add colons.

Example: Paul was not happy: regular attendance and class
                                                    participation.

1. Course requirements are the   a passport.
   following

2. He learned a valuable lesson   He would major in biology.

3. Only one thing was on her mind   In fact, he felt terrible.

4. It's very easy to make lemonade   Addison, Olivia, and Sarah.

5. Here are the most common girl's   I found my wallet that I'd lost.
   names

6. He finally made up his mind   Never argue with your mother.

7. I couldn't believe my luck   passing the test.

8. There is one thing you need to get   Squeeze lemons into water and
                                        add sugar.

Copyright © by Pearson Education, Inc.

Use with textbook pages 396–397.

Complete your own inverted pyramid to narrow your topic down to a single researchable question.

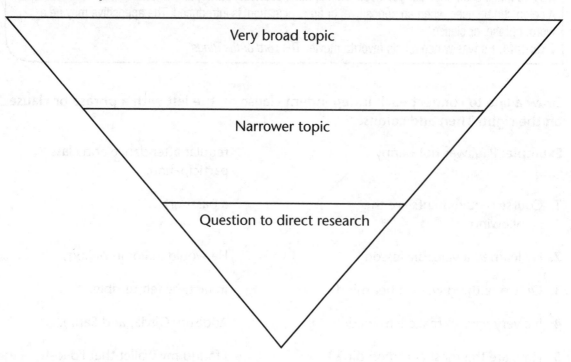

Very broad topic

Narrower topic

Question to direct research

Use the Peer Review Checklist below to obtain feedback from your partner. This feedback will help you edit your final draft.

PEER REVIEW CHECKLIST

☐ Does the first sentence introduce the main research question?

☐ Does the paragraph explain why the topic is interesting?

☐ Does the paragraph explain what the report will be about?

☐ Is the information interesting? Did you want to find out more about the topic?

☐ Is punctuation used correctly?

☐ What changes could be made to improve the paragraph?

Copyright © by Pearson Education, Inc.

How does the sky influence us?

READING 2: "The Girl Who Married the Moon"

VOCABULARY **Literary Words** *Use with textbook page 399.*

> **REMEMBER** A **myth** is a short fictional tale that explains the origins of elements of nature. It has been passed from generation to generation by storytellers. Sometimes myths use **personification**, which gives human qualities to nonhuman animals or things.

Read each sentence. Write *yes* if it uses personification. Write *no* if it does not use personification.

Personification?	Sentences
yes	The house stood watchfully at the end of the lane.
1.	The roof pointed toward the sky.
2.	The city came alive, stretching its limbs, beginning to speak morning words.
3.	There's a sense of humor to the moonlight tonight. It's as if the moon wants us to stay out a little later.

Read the short myth and answer the questions that follow.

> The face of the moon is a mirror. It's carried across the sky by a family, whose skin is so pale and delicate that they can only come out at night, so they don't get burned. The family members pull the moon across the sky. They look at Earth in the mirror. That way they remember where they came from. The <u>smiling face</u> in the moon belongs to the person carrying the moon. The stars twinkle at them in greeting. And the ocean waters wave and say hello when the moon floats by.

4. Underline the words and phrases that personify nonhuman objects or animals.

5. What natural phenomena does the myth try to explain?

_____

Copyright © by Pearson Education, Inc.

Read the paragraph below. Pay attention to the underlined academic words.

My first job was babysitting for a family with two children named Haley and Jack. Haley was still a baby, and her parents instructed me how to change her diaper. I was told their older child Jack was restricted from watching television after 8:00 P.M. Jack did not like when I told him it was time to go to bed. He ignored me and kept watching television. The first night babysitting was hard.

Write the letter of the correct definition next to each word.

Example: ___d___ job

_____ **1.** ignored

_____ **2.** instructed

_____ **3.** restricted

a. did not pay attention to someone or something

b. not allowed to do something

c. taught or showed someone how to do something

d. a particular duty or responsibility that you have

Use the academic words from the exercise above to complete the sentences.

4. Our grandmother _____ us how to play the game of bridge.

5. The protesters were _____ from entering the building.

6. His boring summer _____ was not much fun.

7. Danielle _____ the invitation from her friends since she had to work.

Complete the sentences with your own ideas.

Example: ___My dad_____ instructed me to get out of bed early.

8. I ignored the _____ outside.

9. My ideal job would be _____.

10. Because I'm not an adult, I'm restricted from _____.

Copyright © by Pearson Education, Inc.

WORD STUDY Spelling Long *i* *Use with textbook page 401.*

REMEMBER The long *i* sound can be spelled several different ways. These include *i_e* as in *side*, *igh* as in *tight*, *y* as in *my*, and *i* as in *kind*. Knowing these patterns will help you spell words with the long *i* sound correctly.

Read the words in the box below. Then write each word in the correct column in the chart.

| while | style | isle | tonight | worthwhile | supply |
| grind | tightly | versatile | blind | blight | July |

Long i spelled *i_e*	Long i spelled *igh*	Long i spelled *y*	Long i spelled *i*
while			

Write the letter-sound pattern for long *i* in each word below.

Example: might *long /i/ spelled igh*

1. island _____

2. sign _____

3. slice _____

4. simplify _____

5. sprite _____

6. sigh _____

7. rind _____

8. unify _____

Copyright © by Pearson Education, Inc.

> **REMEMBER** When you read for enjoyment, you aren't just reading for information. You are reading to be entertained by other things, such as the characters, the setting, or the pictures that go with the text.

Read the passage. Then answer the questions that follow.

Anne of Green Gables is one of the most famous fictional characters in literature. One of the best things about her is that she is not perfect. She has several things she can't stand about herself, including her plain name (she adds the "e" to the end of "Ann" to make it seem fancier) and her bright red hair. She is always getting in trouble. But although the book was published in 1908, it is still popular. In fact, thousands of people still visit Canada's Prince Edward Island just to see where Anne was supposed to live!

1. What qualities do you think make a great character?

   _____

   _____

2. Who is your favorite fictional character? Why?

   _____

   _____

3. What is your favorite setting in a novel or story you've read?

   _____

   _____

4. What is the name of the book that you have most enjoyed reading? Why?

   _____

   _____

5. When you read for pleasure, what sorts of texts do you choose to read? Write the name of one book you would like to read for pleasure.

   _____

   _____

Copyright © by Pearson Education, Inc.

Name _____ Date _____

Use with textbook page 410.

Choose the best answer for each item. Circle the letter of the correct answer.

1. The two cousins could have married almost anyone but they fell in love with _____.

   a. the stars   **b.** the sun   **c.** the moon

2. The Moon wanted a wife who was very _____.

   a. patient   **b.** pretty   **c.** quiet

3. After awhile, the Moon's wife became _____.

   a. bored   **b.** sad   **c.** content

4. The people lying facedown on the trail were _____.

   a. suns   **b.** stars   **c.** more moons

5. The Moon decided to let his wife _____.

   a. rest at home   **b.** carry pieces of moon   **c.** watch the sun rise with him

RESPONSE TO LITERATURE *Use with textbook page 411.*

Find a chart showing the moon in orbit around the earth. What part of the lunar cycle is carried by the Moon? What part is carried by his wife? Draw your own diagram to show the answers.

Copyright © by Pearson Education, Inc.

Use with textbook page 412.

> **REMEMBER** Titles of short stories, short poems, myths, legends, songs, interviews, and informational texts are enclosed in quotation marks. Titles of novels, collections of stories, long poems, plays, paintings, movies, magazines, and newspapers are italicized. When writing by hand, you can show italics by underlining the title. If the title has a subtitle, use a colon after the title and capitalize the subtitle.
> **Example:** Don McLean's song "Vincent" was inspired by Van Gogh's *Starry Night*.

Circle the title in each sentence. Then write each title in the space provided, correcting the capitalization and punctuation.

Example: My little sister got scared watching (the wizard of oz) *The Wizard of Oz*

1. The only magazine my mother reads is newsweek. _____

2. Our class is going to see romeo and juliet. _____

3. We sang the Beatles' song hard day's night at the recital. _____

4. We read the road not yet taken in our poetry class. _____

5. Have you seen harry potter on Blu-ray? _____

6. We get the new york times delivered to our door. _____

7. My parents have a copy of Renoir's painting two sisters. _____

8. My mom gave me a collection of short stories called oddly enough.

_____

Copyright © by Pearson Education, Inc.

Punctuation: Hyphens and Dashes *Use with textbook page 413.*

> **REMEMBER** A hyphen (-) is used within words. For example, a two-word adjective before a noun is hyphenated. Hyphens are also used with compound words.
>
> Dashes are longer than hyphens (—) and are used between words. There are no spaces before or after a dash. A pair of dashes is used to draw attention to an interruption in a sentence. Use a single dash to set off an appositive.
>
> **Example:** He didn't like the gift I gave him—a long-sleeved T-shirt.

Add hyphens to the adjectives and compound nouns in the following sentences.

Example: I got a sixty-six on my test.

1. She turns twenty three tomorrow.

2. James is a well known soccer player.

3. My neighbor is a very kind hearted man.

4. Have you responded to my e mail?

Add dashes to set off interruptions or appositives in the following sentences.

Example: Pam sat—alone and by herself—in the corner.

5. Greg ran quickly the quickest he'd ever run before.

6. The cat fat and lazy slept on the sofa as the mouse ran by.

7. The child went everywhere with her teddy bear worn and tattered as it was.

8. My brother as much as I love him drives me crazy sometimes.

Copyright © by Pearson Education, Inc.

Use with textbook pages 414–415.

Complete your own source chart listing citations for a paragraph about a myth.

Paraphrase	Source

Use the Peer Review Checklist below to obtain feedback from your partner. This feedback will help you edit your final draft.

PEER REVIEW CHECKLIST

☐ Is the main idea clearly presented?

☐ Is the main idea supported with details?

☐ Is information from sources paraphrased to support the main idea?

☐ Are in-text citations provided?

☐ Are sources cited correctly?

☐ Are capitalization and punctuation used correctly?

☐ What changes could be made to improve the paragraph?

Copyright © by Pearson Education, Inc.

UNIT 6 — How does the sky influence us?

READING 3: "Return to the Moon" / "No Need to Establish a Moon Base"

VOCABULARY **Key Words** *Use with textbook page 417.*

Write each word in the box next to its definition.

base	crater	lunar	~~mine~~	universe	voyage

Example: _____*mine*_____: dig into the ground in order to get gold, coal, etc.

1. _____: all of space, including the stars and planets

2. _____: a round hole in the ground made by something that has fallen or exploded

3. _____: relating to the moon

4. _____: a long trip, especially in a ship or space vehicle

5. _____: a shelter or headquarters from which an exploration can depart

Use the words in the box at the top of the page to complete the sentences.

6. The phases of the moon are known as the _____ cycle.

7. A journey across the known _____ might take trillions of years.

8. The hikers established their _____ at the bottom of the mountain.

9. Developers _____ in areas where they know coal exists.

10. The ship's captain was looking forward to the _____.

Copyright © by Pearson Education, Inc.

Read the paragraph below. Pay attention to the underlined academic words.

NASA, the National Aeronautics and Space Agency, uses telescopes and spacecraft to <u>investigate</u> our solar system and beyond. NASA scientists <u>research</u> important <u>issues</u> related to Earth, other planets, and the universe. NASA also works to <u>promote</u> public interest in its space programs. It has an excellent website with amazing photographs of the universe.

Write the academic words from the paragraph above next to their correct definitions.

Example: ___*research*___: serious study of a subject that is intended to discover new facts about it

1. _____: help something develop and be successful

2. _____: subjects or problems that people discuss

3. _____: try to find out the truth about something

Use the academic words from the paragraph above to complete the sentences.

4. The group deals with major social _____ like poverty and health care.

5. Alex put up flyers to _____ his new band.

6. The detective began to _____ the crime scene.

7. Sawyer is doing _____ on the way fruit flies balance in the air.

Complete the sentences with your own ideas.

Example: Smoky the Bear promotes ___*forest safety*___.

8. Two important issues facing young people today are

_____.

9. I would like to investigate _____.

10. In school I'm doing research on _____.

Copyright © by Pearson Education, Inc.

WORD STUDY **Acronyms** *Use with textbook page 419.*

REMEMBER Acronyms are created by using the first letters of a phrase, as in *LCD*, liquid crystal display. The letters are usually all capitalized and do not have periods between them.

Read each acronym. Then use a dictionary to find out what it stands for. Write the phrase in the chart.

Acronym	Words that Form Acronym
PIN	*Personal Identification Number*
1. NASA	
2. ATM	
3. FAQ	
4. CEO	
5. WWW	

Write the definition of each acronym. Use a dictionary if needed.

Example: UFO   *unidentified flying object*

6. ZIP (code)   _____

7. TLC   _____

8. Sonar   _____

9. FYI   _____

10. VIP   _____

Copyright © by Pearson Education, Inc.

REMEMBER Taking notes helps you understand and remember new information. Think about your purpose for reading when you take notes. Scan the text and look for the information you need. Don't write in complete sentences.

Read each passage. Then answer the questions that follow.

Zebra finches make great pets. They are small birds that are lively and fun to watch as they fly around in their cages. Their peeps and chirps are quieter than the piercing sound of parrots. Unlike some larger birds that need room to fly around in your house, zebra finches are happy to live in their cages all the time. But owning pets is a big responsibility. Zebra finches need a fairly large cage. They need companionship, so you should buy a pair of them. They need fresh water for drinking and bathing and fresh finch seed. They also like fruits and vegetables.

1. Set a purpose for reading the passage. What do you hope to learn from it?

   _____

   _____

2. Take notes from the passage above.

   _____

   _____

3. What are the three most important facts in the text?

   _____

   _____

4. Write one question you have about the information presented in the passage.

   _____

   _____

5. Why is the strategy of taking notes important to understanding and remembering what you read?

   _____

   _____

Copyright © by Pearson Education, Inc.

COMPREHENSION   *Use with textbook page 424.*

Choose the best answer for each item. Circle the letter of the correct answer.

1. Scientists believe that the moon was originally _____.

   a. part of the sun   **b.** another planet   **c.** part of earth

2. A moon base might allow astronauts to _____.

   a. study the way   **b.** study the moon and the   **c.** learn more about the
   asteroids move   rest of the universe   nearby planet Venus

3. NASA wants colonies of astronauts to eventually live on the moon for _____.

   a. as long as six weeks   **b.** as long as six months   **c.** as long as six years

4. Compared to manned space missions, robotic missions are _____.

   a. more dangerous   **b.** much safer   **c.** about equally safe

5. The two authors disagree _____.

   a. about how to   **b.** about how many space   **c.** if we should explore
   explore space   missions to fly   space further

EXTENSION   *Use with textbook page 425.*

Several countries have launched satellites in the last 50 years. Research five countries and tell when they launched their first satellite.

Country	Date of first satellite launch
United States	*January 31, 1958*

Copyright © by Pearson Education, Inc.

Use with textbook page 426.

REMEMBER Parentheses (( )) can show extra information or set off an abbreviation.
Example: The states (New York and South Carolina) were unhappy with the conditions and voted against the amendment.
Brackets ([ ]) can show changes made to original text.
Example: [They] were unhappy with the conditions and voted against the amendment.
Ellipses (…) can indicate a word or phrase missing from original text.
Example: The states . . . voted against the amendment.

Read the following sentences, adding parentheses where necessary.

Example: He works for the United Nations High Commission on Refugees (UNHCR).

1. The boys Tom, Dick, and Harry collected the money.

2. The New York Stock Exchange NYSE is closed for the holiday.

3. Use parentheses to set of an appositive another name for a noun.

Rewrite each sentence, using brackets with the boldfaced words and ellipses instead of the underlined phrase.

Example: Dr. Smith and Dr. Jones gave a talk <u>at the museum</u> on dinosaurs.

 [The professors] gave a talk . . . on dinosaurs.

4. **Saul's** paper <u>describing plant life on Mars</u> was interesting.

_____

5. His opinion <u>that the economy will improve</u> is not widely held by **the other economists**.

_____

6. **The scientists** completed<u>, with the help of others,</u> their research.

_____

Copyright © by Pearson Education, Inc.

Quoting Sources *Use with textbook page 427.*

> **REMEMBER** When quoting sources in a paper, you can use direct or reported speech. Direct speech is introduced with a reporting verb, often in present tense, such as *says*, *contends*, or *argues*, and is set off with quotation marks. Quotation marks are not used with reported speech. A block quotation is used to quote three or more sentences. Block quotations are introduced with a colon, indented, and don't have quotation marks.

Read the passage below. Follow the instructions for quoting sources.

The National Air and Space Museum
by Stan Keeger

The National Air and Space Museum (NASM), which is part of the <u>Smithsonian Institution</u>, is its most popular attraction. It is conveniently located in <u>Washington, D.C.</u> It holds the largest collection of historic <u>aircraft</u> and <u>spacecraft</u> in the world. It is also a center for research into the history of <u>aviation</u> and <u>spaceflight</u>. Almost all space and aircraft on display are originals. It is a fascinating place to visit.

Example: Quote the first sentence using reported speech.

Keeger states that the NASM is the Smithsonian's most popular attraction.

1. Quote the second sentence using direct speech.

   _____

2. Quote the third, fourth, and fifth sentences using a block quotation.

   _____

   _____

   _____

3. Quote the third sentence using reported speech.

   _____

4. Quote the fourth sentence using direct speech.

   _____

5. Quote the last sentence using reported speech.

   _____

Copyright © by Pearson Education, Inc.

Use with textbook pages 428–429.

Complete your own source chart for a paragraph that includes quotations and citations.

Quotation	Source

Use the Peer Review Checklist below to obtain feedback from your partner. This feedback will help you edit your final draft.

PEER REVIEW CHECKLIST

- ☐ Is the main idea clearly presented?
- ☐ Is the main idea supported with details?
- ☐ Are quotations and citations included?
- ☐ Do quotations flow smoothly within paragraphs?
- ☐ Is a "Works Consulted List" provided?
- ☐ What changes could be made to improve the paragraph?

Copyright © by Pearson Education, Inc.

How does the sky influence us?

READING 4: "Solar Energy—Help from the Sky"

VOCABULARY　**Key Words** *Use with textbook page 431.*

Write each word in the box next to its definition.

beneath	influence	positive	potential	~~renewable~~	solar

Example: ___*renewable*___: able to be replaced by natural processes so that it is never used up

1. _____: someone or something that has an effect on other people or things

2. _____: the possibility that something will develop or happen in a particular way

3. _____: under or below something

4. _____: good or useful

5. _____: relating to the sun or the sun's power

Use the words in the box at the top of the page to complete the sentences.

6. My grandmother had a big _____ on my life because she lived with us when I was a child.

7. I keep my movies on a shelf _____ the television.

8. He has the _____ to be a good football player, but he doesn't practice enough.

9. There are many types of _____ energy, including energy from the sun, wind, and water.

10. Living in different countries has been a(n) _____ experience for Jim because he met many interesting people.

Copyright © by Pearson Education, Inc.

Read the paragraph below. Pay attention to the underlined academic words.

> NASA chose the first seven astronauts in 1959 from a select group of people recommended by the United States military. Now anyone with an education that <u>features</u> a strong background in math and science can apply. One does, though, also have to satisfy the strict mental and physical health <u>criteria</u>. The Astronaut Candidate training program is <u>located</u> in Houston, TX. The program lasts two years and training <u>consists</u> of studying manuals, learning computer systems, and spending time in flight simulators.

Write the academic words from the paragraph above next to their correct definitions.

Example: ___*located*___: in a particular place or position

1. _____: facts or standards used in order to help you judge or decide something

2. _____: is made of or contains a number of different things

3. _____: important, interesting, or typical parts of something

Use the academic words from the paragraph above to complete the sentences.

4. The salesman showed us some interesting _____ of the car.

5. The mysterious object _____ of ice and rock.

6. The world's largest ball of string is _____ in England.

7. That letter to the editor didn't meet the _____ needed to be printed in the paper.

Complete the sentences with your own ideas.

Example: One of my favorite features on the new car is ___*the great stereo*___.

8. My neighborhood is located in _____.

9. One of my criteria for making new friends is _____.

10. My dinner usually consists of _____.

Copyright © by Pearson Education, Inc.

WORD STUDY **Greek and Latin Roots** *Use with textbook page 433.*

> **REMEMBER** Many English words have Greek and Latin roots such as *-gram* (write or record), *photo-* (light), and *poly-* (many). Understanding the meaning of a word root can help you understand the English words that are formed by them.

Look at the chart below. Define each word based on the meaning of its root. Use a dictionary if needed.

Root	Meaning	Word	Meaning
-gram	*write or record*	epigram	*short poem or phrase that expresses ideas in an amusing way*
1. -gram		diagram	
2. photo-		photocopy	
3. photo-		photographer	
4. poly-		polygraph	
5. poly-		polyester	

Underline the Greek or Latin root in each word. Then write the definition of each word based on the meaning of its root. Use a dictionary to check your work.

Example: holo<u>gram</u> *a type of photo made with a laser that looks as if it is not flat when you look at it from an angle*

6. polymorphous _____

7. photojournalism _____

8. polytechnic _____

9. photosynthesis _____

10. cardiogram _____

Copyright © by Pearson Education, Inc.

REMEMBER Connecting ideas will help you understand what the author wants you to know. Look for the main idea in each paragraph and see how it fits in with all the other ideas.

Read the passage. Then answer the questions that follow.

Earth's Rotation: Measuring Day and Night

Ancient astronomers thought the sun and moon were moving around the Earth. In fact, the sun and moon seem to move across the sky because the Earth is rotating, or turning, on its axis. This is called rotation. The Earth's rotation causes day and night. It takes Earth 24 hours to rotate one complete turn. This 24-hour cycle is called a day.

Earth's Revolution: Measuring a Year

As well as rotating, Earth is traveling around the sun. This movement is called a revolution. Earth's path as it revolves around the sun is called its orbit. Earth's orbit takes about 365 days, or one year.

How Sunlight Hits Earth

The equator is the imaginary line around Earth, halfway between the North and South Poles. The equator divides the Earth into two parts: the Northern Hemisphere and the Southern Hemisphere. The warm area around the equator is sometimes called the tropics. Most places outside the tropics have four seasons: winter, spring, summer, and autumn [also called fall].

Why Earth Has Seasons

Earth's axis is tilted as it revolves around the sun. For part of the year, Earth's axis is tilted away from the sun, and for another part of the year, it is tilted toward the sun. The hemisphere that is tilted toward the sun has more hours of daylight than the other hemisphere. The combination of direct sunlight and more hours of daylight creates warmer summer temperatures. The opposite is true for the hemisphere that is tilted away from the sun.

1. Do the section headings give you clues about the main ideas in the text?

_____

2. What is the main idea in each paragraph?

_____

3. How are the ideas similar? What connects them to each other?

_____

4. How can the strategy of connecting ideas help you become a better reader?

_____

Copyright © by Pearson Education, Inc.

COMPREHENSION   *Use with textbook page 438.*

Choose the best answer for each item. Circle the letter of the correct answer.

1. Solar energy was first used _____.
   a. all over the world in the 1970s
   b. in Europe in the 1860s
   c. in ancient Greece and Rome

2. Auguste Mouchout made more steam by using reflectors, which helped to _____.
   a. boil water
   b. make more light
   c. hide the light

3. In the past, people generally wanted to use the fuel that _____.
   a. was most easily available
   b. the space program used
   c. cost the most money

4. As the technology improves, solar panels _____.
   a. are getting bigger
   b. cost more money
   c. cost less money

5. Using solar energy to provide power for a whole city _____.
   a. is not popular
   b. is not possible yet
   c. has happened in a few places

EXTENSION   *Use with textbook page 439.*

Research another kind of renewable energy. Write what type of energy it is on the top line. Then list its good points (pros) and bad points (cons) in the chart.

Renewable Energy:	
Pros	**Cons**

Copyright © by Pearson Education, Inc.

> **REMEMBER** Transitions help you make smoother transitions in your writing. They can be used to add information (*moreover, furthermore, in addition*); to contrast two ideas (*instead, rather, alternatively*); to show cause and effect (*as a result, hence, accordingly*); to clarify (*for example, to illustrate, that is*); to emphasize a point (*for this reason, indeed, in fact*); and to summarize ideas (*in summary, finally, in conclusion*). Transitions begin sentences or clauses and are followed by commas.

Complete the essay with appropriate transitions. More than one answer is possible.

Why the Voting Age Should Be Lowered
by Jen Maddocks

The voting age should be lowered to 16 so that younger people's voices can be heard.

1. _____, younger people would become more active in politics.

2. _____, I believe there is a double standard for young people. We have adult responsibilities without the rights of adults. 3. _____, 16-year-olds have jobs and pay taxes, but cannot take part in electing our officials.

   4. _____, 16-year-olds would contribute more to society if they had the right to vote. 5. _____, their votes might change laws that affect them. 6. _____, young people have a unique perspective that needs to be represented. 7. _____, kids have an interest in laws having to do with schools.

   8. _____, most youths want to be part of the democratic process of the nation. I believe that lowering the voting age will give 16-year-olds a constructive and democratic channel for making their views known.

Copyright © by Pearson Education, Inc.

GRAMMAR **Transitional Clauses** *Use with textbook page 441.*

> **REMEMBER** A transitional clause is a subordinate, or dependent, clause. It is always used with a main, or independent, clause. A transition or transitional phrase begins a transitional clause and is followed by a comma. The transitional clause modifies, or gives more information about, the main clause. A transitional clause is preceded by a semicolon and always follows the main clause.
> **Example:** I don't believe in ghosts; *furthermore,* I think anyone who does is ridiculous.

Connect each main clause on the left with a transitional clause on the right, adding semicolons. Then choose an appropriate transition from the box to complete each sentence.

accordingly	however	finally	likewise	for example
~~nevertheless~~	in addition	in fact	nonetheless	alternatively

Example: Coffee makes me jumpy; _____, I've read them all.

1. I love the Harry Potter books _____, my brother has brown hair.

2. The cat slept all day *nevertheless* _____, I drink two cups a day.

3. Jenny speaks at least two languages _____, he plays the drums.

4. My sister has brown hair _____, I love iced tea.

5. I don't like hot tea _____, it was awake all night.

6. Mark plays the guitar _____, we could go to the movies.

7. We could go to the park _____, bake for 40 minutes.

8. Pour the batter into a pan _____, she knows French and English.

Copyright © by Pearson Education, Inc.

Complete your own main-idea-and-details web for a paragraph that includes a main idea and supporting details.

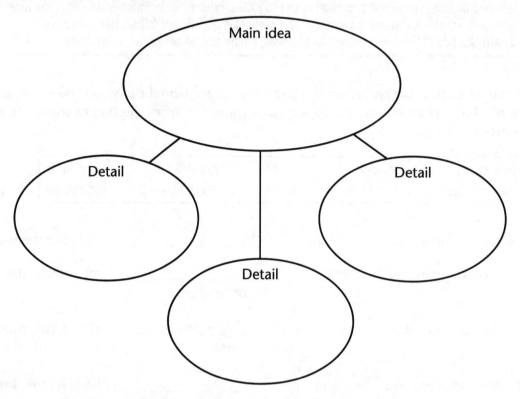

Use the Peer Review Checklist below to obtain feedback from your partner. This feedback will help you edit your final draft.

PEER REVIEW CHECKLIST

☐ Is the main idea clearly presented?

☐ Is the main idea supported with details?

☐ Are specific examples used to explain and support the main idea?

☐ Is the paragraph clearly organized?

☐ Are transitional clauses used correctly?

☐ What changes could be made to improve the paragraph?

Copyright © by Pearson Education, Inc.

WRITING WORKSHOP *Use with textbook pages 448–454.*

Organize your ideas in the graphic organizer below.

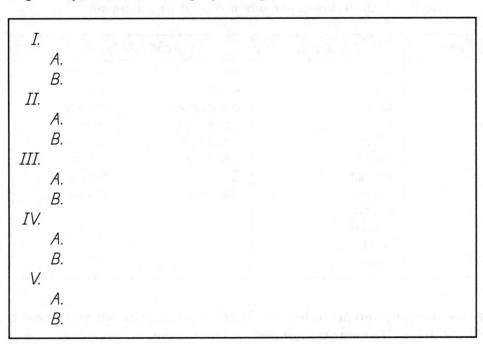

I.
    A.
    B.
II.
    A.
    B.
III.
    A.
    B.
IV.
    A.
    B.
V.
    A.
    B.

Use the Peer Review Checklist below to obtain feedback from your partner. This feedback will help you edit your final draft.

PEER REVIEW CHECKLIST

☐ Was the topic clearly introduced in the first paragraph?

☐ Was the information supported with details and facts?

☐ Did the writer show a thorough understanding of the topic?

☐ Did the writer use transitions to show a logical sequence of ideas?

☐ Did the concluding paragraph sum up the main points in a memorable way?

☐ What changes could be made to improve the essay?

Copyright © by Pearson Education, Inc.

Underline each vocabulary item you know and can use well. Review and practice any you haven't underlined. Underline them when you know them well.

Literary Words	Key Words	Academic Words	
stanza	base	analyze	investigate
rhyme	crater	image	issues
myth	lunar	interpretation	promote
personification	mine	visible	research
	universe	ignored	consists
	voyage	instructed	criteria
	beneath	job	features
	influence	restricted	located
	positive		
	potential		
	renewable		
	solar		

Put a check by the skills you can perform well. Review and practice any you haven't checked off. Check them off when you can perform them well.

Skills	I can . . .
Word Study	☐ recognize and use lexical sets. ☐ recognize and spell words with a long *i*. ☐ recognize words that form acronyms. ☐ recognize and use Greek and Latin roots.
Reading Strategies	☐ analyze text structure 2. ☐ read for enjoyment. ☐ take notes. ☐ connect ideas.
Grammar	☐ use semicolons and colons. ☐ use capitalization, hyphens, and dashes. ☐ use parentheses, brackets, and ellipses; quote sources. ☐ use transitions.
Writing	☐ write an introductory paragraph for a research report. ☐ write a paragraph using paraphrases and citations. ☐ write a paragraph using quotations and citations. ☐ write a paragraph that includes a main idea and details. ☐ write a research report.

Copyright © by Pearson Education, Inc.

TEST 1

DIRECTIONS
Read this selection. Then answer the questions that follow it.

Chinese New Year

1   Everyone is invited to celebrate the Year of the Tiger in Chinatown on February 19 and 20. The two-day event is fun for the whole family.

2   Friday the festival starts with a fashion show. Local musicians will play traditional Chinese tunes in front of the Hong Kong Market. Dancers will take the stage at 5:00 P.M. Children are invited to make tiger masks in honor of the Year of the Tiger.

3   On Saturday, visitors will enjoy the traditional dragon dance. Again, bands will entertain visitors throughout the day. Chefs from several restaurants in Chinatown will offer free samples of food. The evening will end with a huge fireworks display.

1 According to the selection, what is the first event?
- A   Musicians on stage
- B   The dragon dance
- C   A fashion show
- D   Children making masks

2 Where would you most likely find this passage?
- F   In a newspaper
- G   On a highway billboard
- H   In a restaurant menu
- J   On a map of Chinatown

3 When will the dancers perform?
- A   Saturday at 12:00 noon
- B   During the dragon dance
- C   After the fireworks display
- D   Friday at 5:00 P.M.

Copyright © by Pearson Education, Inc.

DIRECTIONS
Read this selection. Then answer the questions that follow it.

Asteroids and Comets

1   Asteroids are part of the solar system. They are pieces of rock and metal. They can be very small or hundreds of kilometers wide. Most of the asteroids in our solar system orbit the sun between Mars and Jupiter.

2   Scientists believe that a big asteroid fell to Earth 65 million years ago. It hit in what is now Mexico. The asteroid was about ten kilometers wide. The asteroid was moving so fast that it made a hole almost 200 kilometers wide. Scientists believe the asteroid caused an explosion that sparked huge fires. The dust and smoke made a dark cloud and blocked sunlight for months. Many kinds of plants and animals probably died.

3   One of the most beautiful sights in the night sky is a comet. A comet is a mass of ice, frozen gases, and dust. Comets orbit the sun. You can see a comet when it is near the sun. The sun heats up the comet. This causes the ice to turn into a cloud of gases with a long tail. Comets do not make their own light. They <u>reflect</u>, or throw back, the sun's light. The brightest comets can be seen only every ten to twelve years.

1 According to the article, asteroids —
  A   orbit the Earth
  B   orbit the sun
  C   orbit Jupiter
  D   orbit the moon

2 Which sentence in paragraph 3 is an opinion?
  F   *One of the most beautiful sights in the night sky is a comet.*
  G   *They reflect, or throw back, the sun's light.*
  H   *A comet is a mass of ice, frozen gases, and dust.*
  J   *You can see a comet when it is near the sun.*

3 In paragraph 3, what words help the reader know what *reflect* means?
  A   sun's light
  B   throw back
  C   make their own light
  D   can be seen

4 Paragraph 2 is mainly about —
  F   the cause of an asteroid falling to Earth
  G   what scientist believe happened when an asteroid hit Earth in the past
  H   the size of an asteroid that hit Mexico
  J   the animals and plants that died when an asteroid hit earth

Copyright © by Pearson Education, Inc.

TEST 3

DIRECTIONS
Read this selection. Then answer the questions that follow it.

Pictures in the Stars

1   Ray tapped his foot as he waited for the doors to open. "I hope this doesn't take too long," he thought. "This stuff is boring." Just then the doors to the planetarium opened and he followed his classmates inside. He looked up and was amazed at the images on the dome-shaped ceiling.

2   "Welcome, students," the guide said. "Today we are going to learn about common constellations. As you know, constellations are patterns of stars. These patterns include the stars that we know best, the ones closest to us. Some of these stars are in patterns that look like people or animals, so people have given them names. Can anyone name one of the best-known constellations?"

3   Ray raised his hand. "One of the best-known constellations is the Big Dipper," Ray said.

4   "That's right. It's called the Big Dipper because it looks like a cup with a long handle. But did you know that the Big Dipper is not a true constellation?" The students shook their heads.

5   "The Big Dipper is not a true constellation because it is part of another constellation called Ursa Major, the Great Bear. The Big Dipper's handle is also the bear's tail." The guide pointed out the image of the Great Bear on the screen above them. Then he changed the screen and asked the students to look for three stars in the pattern of a belt.

6   The guide continued, "Another well-known constellation is Orion. Orion is a character in an ancient Greek myth, or story. He was a great hunter. On a clear night, look for the three stars that make his belt. Once you have found his belt, it is easy to see his right thigh and shoulders." The guide pointed out other constellations. Then he gave each student a booklet to help them find the constellations at home.

7   Ray could hardly wait for the sun to set. He wondered whether he would be able to see all the constellations in the booklet. When night finally came, he went outside with his dad and started searching the sky.

Copyright © by Pearson Education, Inc.

1 Which sentence BEST shows how Ray feels about going to the planetarium at the beginning of the story?

A Ray tapped his foot as he waited for the doors to open.

B "I hope this doesn't take too long," he thought.

C He looked up and was amazed at the images on the dome-shaped ceiling.

D When night finally came, he went outside with his dad and started searching the sky.

2 Paragraph 5 is mainly about —

F Orion

G Ursa Major

H the Big Dipper

J Ray's excitement

3 In paragraph 1, what words help the reader know what *planetarium* means?

A images on the dome-shaped ceiling

B the doors

C looked up and was amazed

D opened and he followed his classmates inside

4 Look at the graphic organizer at the bottom of the page. Which of the following belongs in the box for Event 3?

F The guide described the Big Dipper.

G Ray raised his hand and answered the question.

H The guide told the students about the constellation named Orion.

J The guide explained that the Big Dipper was one of the best-known constellations.

5 According to the selection, if you can find the three stars in the pattern of a belt you can —

A find the constellation Ursa Major

B find the constellation Scorpio

C find the constellation Orion

D find the constellation Ursa Minor

Event 1	Event 2	Event 3	Event 4
The guide showed the students the Big Dipper.	The guide explained that the Big Dipper was part of Ursa Major.		Ray and his father went outside to find constellations.

Copyright © by Pearson Education, Inc.

Test Preparation

Visual Literacy: Smithsonian American
Art Museum Use with textbook pages 456–457.

LEARNING TO LOOK

Look at *Orion in December* by Charles Burchfield on page 457 in your textbook.
The artist felt inspired to paint *Orion in December* after looking out of his bedroom
window on a winter night. Pretend you are looking out of a bedroom window.
How would you paint the same scene?

Example: *I would paint a winter night in December with snow . . .*

_____

_____

_____

_____

_____

_____

INTERPRETATION

Look at *The Eclipse* by Alma Thomas on page 456 in your textbook. If this painting
could give off a sound, what would it be? Explain your answer.

Example: *The sound would be loud and made with drums.*

_____

_____

_____

_____

_____

Copyright © by Pearson Education, Inc.

Look again at *Orion in December* and *The Eclipse* again. Use these two artworks to complete the diagram below. Describe each piece of art in the outer sections of the diagram. Then list the similarities between the two paintings in the center where the two circles overlap.

Charles Burchfield
Orion in December

Similarities

Alma Thomas
The Eclipse

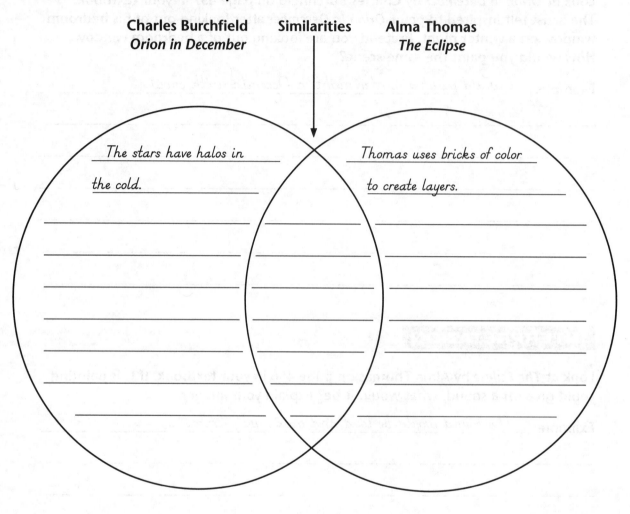

The stars have halos in the cold.

Thomas uses bricks of color to create layers.

Copyright © by Pearson Education, Inc.

Editing and Proofreading Marks

To:	Use This Mark	Example:
add something	$\wedge$	We ate rice, bean$_\wedge^s$ and corn.
delete something	$\mathcal{g}$	We ate rice, beans, and corns.
close space	$\frown$	We $\frown$ ate rice, beans, and corn.
start a new paragraph	$\P$	$\P$ We ate rice, beans, and corn.
add a comma	$\wedge$	We ate rice, beans$_\wedge$ and corn.
add a period	$\odot$	We ate rice, beans, and corn$_\odot$
switch letters or words	$\sim$	We ate rice, baens, and corn.
change to a capital letter	$\underline{\underline{a}}$	we ate rice, beans, and corn.
change to a lowercase letter	$\mathcal{A}$	WE ate rice, beans, and corn.
let the marked text stand	(stet)	We ate rice, beans, and corn. (stet)